THE MODERN SEX MANUAL

by

EDWARD PODOLSKY, M. D.

MEMBER OF: The American Social Hygiene Association, The New York Endocrinological Society, The American Medical and Authors' Association, Formerly Editor of *Progressive Medicine,* Editor of *The Health Review,* Foreign Editor of the *Indian Journal of Venerology.*

CADILLAC PUBLISHING COMPANY,

New York

1949

EDWARD PODOLSKY, M.D., AUTHOR OF:

Medicine Marches On
Young Women Past Forty
Old Age Outwitted
The Diabetes Specialist
Worry and Disease
The War on Cancer, etc.

First Printing 1942
Second Printing 1942
Third Printing 1942
Fourth Printing 1942
Fifth Printing 1942
Sixth Printing 1943
Seventh Printing 1943
Eighth Printing 1943
Ninth Printing 1943
Tenth Printing 1944
Eleventh Printing 1944
Twelfth Printing 1944
Thirteenth Printing 1945

Fourteenth Printing 1945
Fifteenth Printing 1946
Sixteenth Printing 1946
Seventeenth Printing 1946
Eighteenth Printing 1946
Nineteenth Printing 1947
Twentieth Printing 1947
Twenty-First Printing 1947
Twenty-Second Printing 1948
Twenty-Third Printing 1948
Twenty-Fourth Printing 1948
Twenty-Fifth Printing 1948
Twenty-Sixth Printing 1949

Twenty-Seventh Printing...1949
Twenty-Eighth Printing....1950

THE MODERN SEX MANUAL
Copyrighted 1942
CADILLAC PUBLISHING CO.

Printed in the United States of America

PREFACE

Human life consists of drives, and among these forces sex is the greatest. Hunger is the other great drive and the primary object of this urge is to insure man's continuation as an individual. It is hunger which enables man to renew his tissues at regular intervals so that he may continue on this earth as an individual.

Sex is the great human drive which enables man to continue on earth as a species. The biological object of the sexual emotion is to provide man with earthly immortality. Sexual feeling is deeply ingrained in all living human beings. It is not an emotion to be shunned, to be suppressed and left in the dark.

A physician is constantly in touch with a great variety of sexual problems, and it is these that I have attempted to answer and solve in the present book. As with other biological sciences many important advances have been made in sexology within the past few years. Among these may be mentioned the estrogen treatment of impotence in the male and frigidity in the female, the correction of infantilism in both sexes by means of sex hormones, the psychological aspects of sex and the increasing importance of sexuality in everyday life. These have been discussed in the present book.

It has also been my object to make the contents as practical as possible. There is no room for airy theories in a manual designed for everyday use. The most frequently asked questions have been given consideration.

EDWARD PODOLSKY, M.D.

Brooklyn, N. Y.

CONTENTS

PART I

DESIGNS FOR A SUCCESSFUL MARRIAGE

PART II

OVERCOMING SEXUAL DIFFICULTIES

PART III

MARITAL PROBLEMS OF THE LATER YEARS

PART IV

MODERN ASPECTS OF THE SEXUAL QUESTION

LIST OF ILLUSTRATIONS

PART I

DESIGNS FOR A SUCCESSFUL MARRIAGE

Chapter 1

ARE YOU FIT OR UNFIT FOR MARRIAGE?

The average young couple today realizes that marriage is quite a serious undertaking. There are questions and problems which arise in every-day life that require intelligent guidance and explanation. Unnecessary suffering and hardships have been encountered by many couples whose unwarranted shyness, especially on sexual problems, has prevented them from obtaining the solution to their troubles. From an extensive file of questions, gathered in a long and successful medical practice, the most commonly asked have been selected for discussion in this book. Without any further comment let us answer the first query.

Is Love a Static Emotion?

Love is not a static emotion. It varies with the passing of the years. It changes with one's emotional status and interests.

Would you say that there are many different kinds of love?

"Precisely. Most people think only of romantic love when they think of love at all. But love is much more than that. It is one of the earliest emotions experienced by a human being. In infancy there is an overwhelming love of self, primarily love centered about nutritional aspects. The infant is almost constantly feeding, and any interruption of this process is resented. The process of ingestion is accompanied by a great deal of labial activity, and such authorities as Freud and Brill are of the opinion that this labial activity in feeding is a very pleasurable experience.

"As the child grows older his love interests change, but still they are primarily centered about himself. He is in the Narcissistic stage, that is, the self-love stage. Instead of labial activity as a means of attaining pleasurable sensations there are muscular play and activity. Childhood games are an adequate love outlet for the preschool child. However, at this time there are also the beginnings of love of parents.

"According to Freud and Stekel there is a very strong homosexual component in all normal pre-adolescent children. This homosexual love is quite natural. Boys tend to associate with boys, and girls with girls, and their love interests take the form of esteem for their friends. Hero-worship in childhood is a form of homosexual love.

"As the child enters puberty there is an awakening of his internal sex glands; they begin to manufacture and secrete the chemical materials which cause a boy's voice to deepen and a girl's form to fill out. It is at this time that a youngster begins to experience the first faint stirrings of heterosexual love.

"The further along into adolescence a child goes, the greater this heterosexual love becomes. According to such endocrinologists as Berman and Hoskins, the first awakening of romantic love has a purely endocrinal basis; it is based on the secretions of the internal sex glands."

Would you say that romantic love has a purely glandular basis?

"The endocrinologists would have you believe that, but there would seem to be much more to it than that. It is true that the glandular secretions are largely responsible for heterosexual love manifestations, but there are other factors, too, such as emotional and mental conditioning and experience.

"As the boy and girl enter adult stages, romantic love gives rise to thoughts of marriage, which, of course, is and should be the natural outcome of love."

But is it actually as simple as all that? Does merely the love of a man for a woman act as the motivating factor in the desire to get married?

"No. There is much more to it than that. There are several schools of thought in regard to the purposes of marriage. Thus Alfred Adler believes that, in addition to love, a sympathetic nature in the one who is loved plays an important part in maintaining love. Freud firmly asserts that romantic love is conditioned or prepared for, in infancy and childhood. In other words, the girl who loves her father will seek a father-type of lover. The boy who was firmly attached to his mother will seek out a girl who reminds him of his mother. Similarly, a girl who was very warmly attached to her brother will most likely fall in love with a man who is as much like her brother as he possibly can be. According to Alice Ruhle, romantic love is fed by the desire to acquire greater self-esteem. A man will fall in love with a woman because he will then acquire a mate, who will bring greater responsibilities and with these greater self-esteem. Wilhelm Stekel is of the opinion that love for others is merely a transference to another person of love of self."

Marriage being the natural outcome of the love of a man for a woman, are there not certain factors that have to be taken into careful consideration before marriage is entered into? Specifically: Are there not certain physical conditions which interdict or forbid marriage?

"There are, and among them I would mention tuberculosis in its active form, disabling diseases of the heart, untreated syphilis and gonorrhea, certain kidney ailments, serious diseases of the brain and nervous system, and profound disturbances of metabolism, such as diabetes and diseases of the thyroid. We shall consider each in turn.

"Tuberculosis, when it is still active, is a definite menace to the healthy partner, since it can be transferred from one person to another with ease. Secondly, it is a serious handicap to the tuberculous partner, because this disease is so debilitating that it will not permit him to carry out his marital obligations without exceedingly grave consequences. But even should both these conditions be met successfully, there is still another danger to consider: namely, that tuberculosis will be passed onto the offspring of such a union.

"Heart disease may be chronic or acute. In cases of chronic rather mild forms of heart disease, marriage is permissible. However, in cases of acute, failing hearts, where there is serious disturbance in the rate and rhythm of the heart action, where there are frequent fainting spells and attacks of pain in the region of the heart, leaving the patient gasping for breath, marriage is entirely out of the question.

"The question of the relation of heart disease to marriage is a most important one. Heart specialists are quite often called upon to determine the efficiency of the heart in persons about to get married. In the woman the determination of the organic status of the heart is extremely important because pregnancy puts an added burden on that organ.

"The most common heart conditions that are met with in the clinics are mitral stenosis, myocarditis, aortic regurgitation, mitral regurgitation and disturbed heart rhythm. Let us consider each of these briefly.

"Mitral stenosis means a narrowing of the mitral valves (the valves in the left side of the heart), and it is caused by various infectious diseases, mostly rheumatic fever. It is a disease of the young and is rather common. Thus young women have to give this form of heart disease very careful consideration.

"Heart specialists feel that the heart affection which most often causes dangerous complications during pregnancy is that associated with mitral stenosis following rheumatic fever. However, this does not mean that every woman who has had rheumatic fever, and whose heart has been affected as a result, should not be allowed to have children. The heart may have recovered to such an extent that bearing a child will not be a dangerous undertaking.

"Dr. J. Mackenzie, who was one of the greatest of heart specialists, laid down four guides for women in regard to this type of heart disorder. These are:

"1. When ten or fifteen years after the rheumatic attack, the heart is making a good response to ordinary daily efforts, if there is no swelling of the feet, a woman may marry with a fair assurance of safety.

"2. When the heart is normal in size, not too excitable, and capable of a fair response to effort, a woman may marry. However, she should lead a somewhat restricted life, avoiding such efforts as tend to bring on breathlessness or palpitation.

"3. When an attack of rheumatic fever has so crippled the heart that a woman cannot meet the ordinary tasks of daily life without breathlessness on slight exertion, rapid pulse, or easily excited palpitation, there is definite danger in getting married.

"4. When the heart is large or irritable, and when effort readily brings on palpitation and breathlessness, marriage should be avoided.

"Myocarditis means an inflammation of the heart muscle. When the heart muscle is so damaged by such inflammation that the ordinary tasks of life cause breathlessness, marriage is to be forbidden. Fortunately it is the least common of heart ailments found in the young and it is among the most dangerous of heart ailments.

"Aortic regurgitation means that, because the aortic valves of the heart fail to close properly during the heartbeats, some of the blood leaks back into the heart. In such a case, marriage may or may not be permitted, according to the amount of damage to the valves. If the heart is not enlarged, or but slightly enlarged, and if the response to effort is good, there is no danger. If, on the other hand, the heart is definitely enlarged and there is a distinct limitation of response to effort, marriage is entirely out of the question.

"It is possible to evaluate the efficiency of the heart, according to a simple test devised by Dr. H. Pardee. The person to be tested is made to exercise, standing with feet separated and swinging a ten-pound dumb-bell held in both hands. He swings this dumb-bell over the head twenty times, repeating the exercise after about one or two seconds rest. A person with an efficient heart can do this without any distress. The pulse will rise to the rate of 120 a minute or less, but by the end of a minute it will return to normal.

"If twenty swings of the ten-pound weight should cause evident distress, shown by flushing of the face, extreme difficulty in breathing and a very fast heart beat which does not return to normal within two minutes, then a person may be said to have an inefficient heart. In such a case marriage is considered to be a hazardous undertaking.

"Diseases of the kidneys are rather serious handicaps, so far as marriage is concerned. Chronic interstitial nephritis, or Bright's Disease, is a contraindication or warning against marriage. The constant presence of albumin in the urine and markedly decreased efficiency of renal function as determined by the P.S.P. test, mean that the kidneys are far from normal and that they will not permit a normal married life. However, when these tests reveal but slight kidney irritation, marriage is permissible.

"Active syphilis is revealed by the presence of a positive Wassermann test and, when this is the case, marriage is entirely out of the question. As a matter of fact, many states now require a negative Wassermann before marriage certificate is issued. Syphilis is a serious constitutional ailment, and it is passed on to the offspring. For this reason uncured syphilis is a barrier to marriage.

"Similarly, uncured gonorrhea is an obstacle to a happy marriage. It is primarily a disease of the genital organs causing inflammatory changes in very vital parts. Quite often it is the direct cause of sterility. A thorough examination of the secretions from the genital organs should be made for the presence of the gonorrhea germ. If it is present, treatment should be instituted at once. Only when these secretions are absolutely free from gonorrheal germs may marriage be permitted.

"There are certain diseases of the brain and nervous system which, unfortunately, do not yield

The Glands that Generate Sex Vigor and Vitality in Your Body

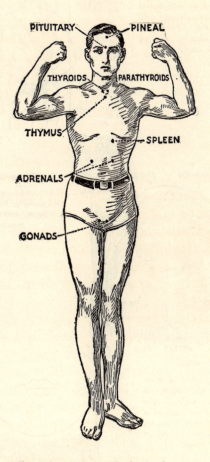

The endocrine (internal) glands of a man

How the Endocrine Glands Produce Sex Maturity

The development of "secondary" characteristics—the outward signs of femininity—controlled by the glands; but if these are stimulated into action too soon, the close of sex life will also be reached too soon.

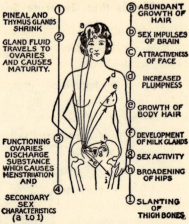

PINEAL AND THYMUS GLANDS SHRINK

GLAND FLUID TRAVELS TO OVARIES AND CAUSES MATURITY.

ⓐ ABUNDANT GROWTH OF HAIR

ⓑ SEX IMPULSES OF BRAIN

ⓒ ATTRACTIVENESS OF FACE

ⓓ INCREASED PLUMPNESS

ⓔ GROWTH OF BODY HAIR

ⓕ DEVELOPMENT OF MILK GLANDS

ⓖ SEX ACTIVITY

ⓗ BROADENING OF HIPS

FUNCTIONING OVARIES DISCHARGE SUBSTANCE WHICH CAUSES MENSTRUATION AND

SECONDARY SEX CHARACTERISTICS (a to i)

ⓘ SLANTING OF THIGH BONES

The Supra-Renal Glands

The supra-renals give vigor and activity; their disease, in a woman, makes her appear masculine.

LEFT SUPRA-RENAL · DIAPHRAGM · SPINE · RIGHT SUPRA-RENAL

SPLEEN · LIVER

LEFT KIDNEY · ARTERY · VEIN · RIGHT KIDNEY

INTESTINES

The thyroid (right) is associated with sex vigor, in either sex, as well as the nourishment of the body as a whole. The glands form an interlocking system, acting on each other.

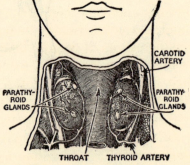

CAROTID ARTERY

PARATHYROID GLANDS

PARATHYROID GLANDS

THROAT · THYROID ARTERY

to treatment. Among these are Huntington's chorea, Little's Disease, amytrophic lateral sclerosis, and chronic encephalitis. As time goes on, these ailments tend to increase in severity. Marriage is always an added burden to the nervous system and, for this reason, tends to aggravate these diseases. The bearing of normal children is often impossible when any one of these nervous disabilities is present. For this reason the presence of a serious ailment of the brain or nervous system is a contraindication of marriage.

"Severe metabolic diseases, such as diabetes and hyperthyroidism, also are obstacles to a successful marriage. The result of a severely damaged pancreas, when it is the direct cause of diabetes, may be transmitted to one's offspring. However, when the diabetes is mild, and easily controlled by insulin and diet, there is no reason why the person so afflicted cannot marry.

"Hyperthyroidism, or overactive thyroid, is a serious ailment. Oversecretion on the part of this important gland at the base of the neck has a disastrous effect on the heart and nervous system. A person with this trouble is exceedingly nervous and very high-strung. Thus, while this gland is overfunctioning, marriage should not be considered, as it would tend to aggravate the condition. An operation usually is sufficient to curb the overactivity of the gland and restore the body to its normal equilibrium. When this is accomplished, marriage becomes possible."

All these factors are important and should be given careful consideration by every couple con-

templating marriage. Suppose all conditions relating to health have been met successfully, are there tests which make it possible to find out whether or not a married couple can have children?

"There are. It is quite a simple matter to determine whether or not a man is sterile by examining a specimen of his seminal fluid. If there is a total absence of sperm in his seminal fluid, or if the sperm are deformed and very few in number, we can say that he is sterile and will be incapable of having children.

"In women it is a bit more difficult to determine sterility. There are many more factors that have to be considered. If her Fallopian tubes are constricted; if she has a tumor or growth of the ovaries or the womb; or if her internal sex organs are infantile in size and development; in any of these instances she is very likely to be incapable of having children. A thorough examination by a gynecologist will usually give the answer. The potency of the Fallopian tubes can be determined by means of the Rubin test, which consists of blowing air into the tubes and taking an X-ray picture. Tactile examination will reveal the presence of any growth, and inspection tells whether or not the genital organs are underdeveloped."

There is a great deal of confusion about marriage between blood relations. Are such marriages likely to turn out unfavorably?

"The question of marriage between blood relations, particularly between first cousins, has been raised time and again. There are a great many silly superstitions about such marriages. There is no reason why first cousins should not marry if they are perfectly healthy, physically and mentally. If there is some defect in the family, a marriage between close relatives may intensify this defect. Otherwise, there is no valid reason for forbidding marriage between close relatives.''

What about marrying outside one's race and religion?

"This is a very complex problem. Interreligious and interracial marriages have been discussed for a great many years. Before such a marriage is entered into, careful thought should be given to its consequences. If there is a strong, abiding love between the man and the woman who are about to contract such a marriage, and if the question of the religious upbringing of the children can be settled satisfactorily, such a marriage can turn out to be successful. Usually the best thing is to allow the children to choose their own religion after reaching puberty. In such marriages, tolerance for each other's beliefs is a very important prerequisite.

"Interracial marriages are a greater problem. It should be realized that the offspring of such marriages are half-breeds, and that because of this fact they will be subjected to some unhappiness. Interracial marriages are frowned upon by some states, in some instances, even forbidden. Social conventions do not sanction them.''

Is not the economic factor also a very important one? Should there not be some firm economic foundation for marriage?

"It is best that there should be. Marriage in most cases presents many economic problems. It is an enterprise which requires money. Some couples, to be sure, have been used to high standards of living and require considerable money for a successful marriage. Others are used to relatively lower standards and can live happily on very little money. In any event, however, the money problem is present and must be handled wisely and well.

"It is desirable that some money be put aside to furnish a home. It may not be a very pretentious home, perhaps only a room or two, but at least the young people will have some place they can call their own.

"A steady source of income is also to be considered. The husband should have some sort of job to keep the home fires going. The wife, if she has a position when married, may consider it worth while to retain it and help along with the family finances. Such an arrangement often works out very well. Many modern women have careers which they are loth to give up when they marry. There is no reason why they should do so.

"The idea that 'woman's place is in the home' is now considered old-fashioned by a great many couples. Modern science and invention have simplified household tasks so that these can now be performed with a minimum of time and effort. Thus a woman has time for other work. Many successful women artists, writers, lawyers and doctors are happily married. They continue to work at their two careers, their profession and their marriage, with a large measure of success.''

Does the mental attitude toward marriage play an important part?

"It undoubtedly does. A wrong mental attitude toward marriage often tends to undermine it. Here is a rather common example: A girl grows up thinking that sex is something vulgar. In such a case, often the parents are responsible for this fault. They did not take the time to teach her the true meaning of sex, so she picked up the wrong notions from ill-informed companions. When such a girl marries, she does so principally for social reasons, and she regards the sexual side of marriage as indecent. In brief, she is totally unfit for marriage. She has peculiar ideas about the sex act, considering it simply as a requirement for having children, and nothing more. She has made up her mind that coitus is something to be endured with a martyr's resignation, not to be enjoyed. In other words, she is emotionally unprepared for marriage, and she should not enter into it.''

Are there other unhealthy mental attitudes that tend to destroy the chances of a happy marriage?

Unfortunately, there are quite a few of them. There is a type of young woman who has been made to feel from early childhood that this is a man's world. Her attitude toward sex is one of indignation and disgust. She fails to realize that sex plays a very important part in marriage and, for this reason, she will not make a success of it. Taboos and inhibitions forced upon a woman during her adolescent years are often so deeply ingrained that they become a source of trouble later on.''

Conceded that fitness for marriage depends upon physical, mental and emotional compatibility, are there not biological factors that have to be considered? For instance, what is the best age for marriage?

''The best time to get married is when men and women are at their physical and mental prime. The sexual urge may be used as a reliable guide. In man it is greatest between 20 and 40, especially between 25 and 35. I should say that the best age for a man to get married is between 26 and 35. In women the sex urge develops somewhat earlier, and for that reason, she should marry between the ages of 23 and 30.

''Marriage is a cooperative undertaking. Some-one has compared marriage to a yoke which two individuals are bearing. Often this yoke does not weigh evenly upon both necks. One neck may be more tender than the other; one may pull forward, while the other pulls backward. One may have an arc of the yoke ill-fitting, irritating, causing friction, sores, calloused areas. Most of the factors that tend to cause discomfort in marriage depend upon human behavior, which is the sum total of one's reactions toward life. The difficulties in marriage constitute special cases in which numerous factors arising from personal experience can be evaluated.

''Marriage is a linkage between two independent beings. In the successful marriage each individual preserves a measure of independence while, at the same time the two personalities fuse enough so that there is a common bond, or tie. During marriage there is a flow of emotional interest which, in each partner, recognizes and makes full allowance for the welfare, happiness and personality of the other.

"It is evident that a man and woman, when married, are a pair of individuals who possess infinite potentials for reaction. Their psychological constitutions, as well as their physical organisms, are not fixed and static. They possess tremendous variables which, in turn, are subject to pressures, both from within and from without, under varying circumstances and conditions which make it difficult to predict results. Something is always arising to alter the complexion of things, and the ability to adjust oneself harmoniously to these changing conditions is essential to success in marriage.

"Yet there is a great deal more to marriage than that. The mechanics of marriage, or more specifically, its biological foundation, requires some explanation. This will be the next subject discussed."

Chapter 2

THE MECHANICS OF MARRIAGE

"There is really no mystery at all about the mechanics of marriage, or to use another term, the biology of marriage. It is true that having children is one of the most important functions of marriage, a prime biological function. In nature, the male of the species produces sperm cells and the female, eggs or ova.

"These sex cells, unlike in every detail, must be brought into intimate contact to produce the phenomenon known as fertilization. When the female sex cell, or ovum, is fertilized, it begins to increase in size and in complexity. In time it evolves into a living being. But before the male sex cells or spermatozoa unite with the female sex cell, or ovum, there must be a physical union between the male and the female. This is a process known as coitus, or sexual intercourse, and is accomplished by the union of the male and female sex organs. Both male and female sex organs consist of external and internal parts."

What are the external parts of the male sex organs?

"These consist of the penis, the testes and the scrotum. The penis is the tubular part of the sex organs, the testes are the two egg-shaped organs suspended in the bag, or scrotum."

What are the functions of each of these parts?

"The testes are the manufacturing plants of the male sex cells or spermatozoa. There are two testes, a right and a left. Generally they measure about two inches in length and slightly over one inch in width. They vary, of course, as the sizes of men vary. In the testes are manufactured a secretion, or hormone, which is required by the male body for its strength and other characteristic features. This hormone causes a man to have a lower and stronger tone of voice than a woman, is responsible for the growth of his beard, and contains the essence of his 'maleness.' In the condition known as castrates, or eunuchs, this hormone is lacking and we have the typical picture of a sexless creature, beardless, having a high-pitched voice, and possessing traits which are definitely more feminine than masculine.

"The scrotum is the bag which protects the testes. The scrotum is not always the same size, because it is composed of very fine muscular tissue which enables it to contract or expand. This change in size is due mainly to temperature variations, and its primary function is to protect the testes from too great a temperature fluctuation.

"The third component of the external sex organs of the male is the penis, or organ of copulation. Copulation means simply physical union. The primary function of the penis is to effect penetration into the female genital tract and convey the seminal fluid from the male to the female. For this reason the penis has the shape most suitable for this purpose. It is attached by strong fibers to the bones of the pelvis or lower part of the hip bones. The penis consists of a head or glans, a body, or shaft, that is pierced by a channel called the urethra through which the seminal fluid travels; and strong muscular fibers, at the base, which impart extra strength to its erectile powers.

"The entire penis, particularly the tip, or glans, is supplied with numerous nerve endings, which, when stimulated, cause the penis to become engorged with blood. When this happens the penis becomes turgid and erect. This makes it possible to perform the sex act.

"The penis is ordinarily relaxed and in a flaccid condition. Because its structure is spongy in nature, it can become filled up with blood in a comparatively short time. Under the stimulus of sexual excitement the penis not only becomes erect; it also increases in size and width."

What is the size of the normal penis?

"This is a question which has been troubling a great many men. Some who have been under the impression that their penis was below normal in size have suffered terribly from an inferiority complex. Others have thought themselves incapable of performing the sex act because of the silly notion that their external organs were substandard in size and development. The penis, when in the relaxed state, measures about three and three quarter inches. In circumference it is about an inch. It may vary a half inch, and still be within normal limits."

ernal and internal parts. The external female x organs consist of the outer lips, or *labia ajora,* the inner lips or *labia minora,* the clitoris, nd the hymen.''

What function does each of these parts perform?

''The outer lips, or *labia majora,* are the outermost parts of the external female sex organs, serving as a protection. In virgins, these outer lips meet almost in the center and serve as an efficient covering for all the other organs.

''When the outer lips are separated, the inner lips, or *labia minora,* come into view. These are parallel to the outer lips, are much smaller in size, and vary greatly in structure.

''At the upper angle of the vulva, or external organs, where the two inner lips come together we find the clitoris. It may be said to be a very small penis, for it is quite similar to that organ in structure. It is only about one-fifth of an inch in size. Like the penis, it is composed of erectile tissue, and is richly supplied with a great many nerve endings, which render it very sensitive to touch and stimulation.

''The clitoris is an extremely important organ. It is the chief seat of sexual feeling in women. The vaginal walls and the neck of the womb are also seats of voluptuous sensation in the female, but the clitoris seems to be the most sensitive. During sexual intercourse it is constantly being stimulated by the penis. This causes it to become erect and firm. The direct stimulation of the clitoris is in great part responsible for the or-

What do the internal male sex organs consist of?

''The internal male sex organs are the seminal vesicles and the prostate. There are two seminal vesicles, each a sac-like organ, and they are situated at the base of the bladder. Connected with special ducts to the testes, they serve two purposes. First they serve as a storage place for the spermatozoa, and second they manufacture a thick gummy substance which is mixed with the sperm cells to give the fluid greater consistency and volume.

''The prostate is situated at the base of the bladder. It is shaped somewhat like a horsechestnut. This organ takes part in the process of ejaculation by contracting and forcing the seminal fluid out. During this process it adds to the seminal fluid its own secretion, a thin, milky white liquid, alkaline in reaction. The prostatic secretion is believed to have an activating influence on the spermatozoa.''

Does the spermatozoa have a considerable distance to travel?

''Yes. It is born in the testes, suspended in the protective scrotum. Thence it travels through twenty feet of the epididymis, which lies at the base of each testicle. At its lower end the epididymis empties into a larger duct, called the *vas deferens.* This duct curves upward in the scrotum, passes for some distance through a canal in the groin, and then enters the lower part of the abdomen. Here it turns down again and passes over the base of the bladder, finally opening up into the main channel, or urethra. This is a long journey to travel, and all the passages must remain clear.''

There āre several other questions in this general connection. Here is the first: Is there any relation between the size of the penis and a man's sexual power?

''Only when the penis is actually infantile in size and development owing to lack of internal secretions of the endocrine and sexual glands, is there any appreciable decrease in sexual power. When this is the case, the man's physical development is also arrested. There is no growth of hair on his face, his voice is weak and high-pitched, and his muscular development is poor. However, when the penis is only slightly smaller than usual, there is no diminution in sexual power.''

What is the volume of the average secretion of seminal fluid?

''About 1 c.c.. This amount consists of spermatozoa and secretions from the prostate and the seminal vesicles.''

Approximately how many spermatozoa does this amount of seminal fluid contain?

''About half a billion. This is an immense number when you consider that only one spermatozoön is necessary to fertlize the female sex cell, or ovum. The mortality among the spermatozoa, however, is so great that Nature, to make sure that fertilization will occur, furnishes this prodigious number.''

What appearance has a spe

''It has quite a characteris sembling when seen under th elongated tadpole. The spermato three parts: a rounded head; a sm and a long slender, tapering tail. E specific function. The head and th contain the chromosomes and genes, which impart the physical and men teristics to one's offspring. If these ch and genes are perfect, a normal heal will result. If they are defective, the will contain some mental or physical defe long tapering tail is solely for the purp locomotion. When it moves rapidly from s side it propels the spermatozoön to its des tion, the ovum, which it finds and fertilizes.''

Is it possible for the seminal fluid to conta no spermatozoa?

''It is, and, when this is the case, the man is sterile. He cannot have children.''

Does this also mean that he is impotent, that he lacks sexual desire?

''No. A man may be capable of having an erection and sexual intercourse, and still be sterile. There is no relation between sterility and impotence. Different factors are responsible for each condition.''

Are the female sex organs analogous to the male? Do they consist of external and internal parts?

''Yes, they are analogous, being divided into

gasm, or sexual excitement, in the woman. Its extreme importance should be realized, for failure by the husband to bring direct contact to bear upon the clitoris will often result in lack of sexual response by his wife.

"About an inch below the clitoris, between the lower edges of the smaller, inner lips, is situated the opening of the vagina. In the virgin this opening is partially covered by a membrane known as the hymen, or, more popularly, as the maidenhead. This membrane is not a whole sheet of uninterrupted substance, but is perforated, even in the virgin. The hymen has no special function, so far as is known.

"These, in brief, are the female external sex organs. The vagina, or birth canal, is the direct connection between the external and the internal sex organs. It thus forms a continuous path of communication between the womb and the external world. The vagina is an exceedingly important organ. It is the receptive organ, in that it receives the penis, or male sex organ, during the act of copulation. During the act of ejaculation, the spermatozoa are discharged into the vagina and, from there, begin their upward journey to the womb, ultimately reaching the ova or eggs for fertilization.

"The vagina varies in size, from one-half an inch in the virgin, to two inches in the married woman who has borne children. Its walls contain many folds, known as rugae, and, as a result, it is very elastic. This is to be expected, for the vagina is the channel through which the child is born, and during this process it is subjected to a great deal of stretching.

"At either side of the vaginal openings are Bartholin's glands. These and other small glands within the vagina produce a viscid secretion when libido, or sexual feeling, is aroused and this secretion acts as a lubricant at the beginning of intercourse. Unless the libido is first aroused by fondling and petting so as to cause these glands to function, intercourse may be painful or impossible."

Can it be said that the inner end of the vagina comes in contact with the internal sex organs of the woman?

"Yes, the upper portion of the vagina comes in direct contact with the neck of the womb, which projects directly into the vagina. The womb is the most important organ from the child-bearing point of view. In it the child is developed and harbored until the time comes for it to be born."

What sort of organ is the womb?

"The womb, or uterus, is a pear-shaped organ consisting of a body and a neck. The wider part, the body, is the uppermost section of the womb; the narrower part, or neck, is situated at the bottom. The uterus is rather small, varying from two to three inches in length, and from two to two and one-half inches in width. It has very thick muscular walls, capable of expanding to many times the original size."

Is the womb connected with any other organs?

"Yes, it is connected with the Fallopian tubes,

which in turn are connected with the ovaries, thus forming a complete circuit. These Fallopian tubes, one on each side of the womb, are about five inches in length and very narrow. Where they approach the ovaries, the ends of the Fallopian tubes have fringe-like projections which are in close contact with the ovaries. These are for the purpose of insuring safe passage of the ova from the ovary to the tubes."

Do the ovaries manufacture the ova or female sex cells?

"Yes, the ovaries are two glands, situated on either side of the womb, and connected with it by means of the Fallopian tubes. They manufacture the ova, or eggs, just as the testes manufacture the spermatozoa, or male sex cells.

"The ovaries are oval in shape and about one and one-half inches in length. In a female child, at birth, they contain up to 100,000 immature ova, but at maturity the total number may be reduced to 40,000 or less. Each woman, after she has reached puberty, has a definite menstrual cycle consisting, as a rule of twenty-eight days. This means that once each month, from puberty to the menopause, or time when this process ceases, one of the minute sacs or follicles which surround each egg becomes enlarged, migrates to the surface of the ovary and bursts, releasing the ovum into the abdominal cavity.

"Just how this egg finds its way into the fimbriated, or fringed, open end of the Fallopian tube is a mystery, since it has no means of propulsion and must depend upon the movements of the cilia, or minute hair-like fringes, of other cells for its transportation. It is believed, however, that when the follicle is about to burst, it exerts a sort of specific attraction, called *chemotaxis,* which causes the fimbriated opening of the tube to place itself over the bursting follicle so that the cilia of the cells may propel the ovum into the tube.

"The picture is beginning to become clear now. Is this a correct description? The testes manufacture the spermatozoa, and the ovaries manufacture the ova. A union of a spermatozoön and an ovum is necessary for fertilization and reproduction. To bring these two cells together is the object of sexual intercourse."

"Precisely. Sexual acts are essentially biological. They are required for the perpetuation of the race. The sexual instinct is inborn in every normal man and woman. It is not indecent and vulgar if it is not perverted. It is as natural as eating and drinking and sleeping. From the biological point of view, a sexual union is the first step in the Odyssey of a wonderful journey of the male sex cell in search of the female sex cell.

"After ejaculation has occurred, the spermatozoa are in the vagina traveling upward to the mouth of the womb. Meanwhile the ovum has ripened in the ovary. The most amazing thing is that, while billions of spermatozoa are produced by the testes, only one egg a month is matured in the ovaries, and this in one ovary at a time."

What sort of object is the human ovum, or egg?

"It is round in shape, very much unlike the spermatozoön. It has no tail, and therefore no power of locomotion. Thus it remains stationary and passive. It is much larger than the spermatozoön, and must be sought out by the much smaller, and much more active, male sex cell."

How is the ovum fertilized?

"While the ovum is making its passage through the tube, if spermatozoa have recently been deposited near the mouth of the womb during intercourse, one of these spermatozoa swims forth to meet it, pierces its outer membrane and, uniting with it, fertilizes it. Only one spermatozoön is required to fertilize the egg. When this has occurred the outer covering of the fertilized egg coagulates and makes penetration by any other spermatozoön impossible. Fertilization always takes place while the ovum is passing through the tube, and not after it reaches the womb."

What happens after the ovum is fertilized?

"It attaches itself to the wall of the womb, where it gradually develops into a living human being. For a period of nine months this embryo increases in size, slowly taking on human form. At the end of the period of gestation, or pregnancy, birth takes place."

Is there still more to learn along these same general lines?

"Yes, there is still a great deal more to learn. Next will be presented a discussion of the sex act itself. Sexual union is not wholly an instinctive performance. There are a number of missteps which may be taken innocently, but which in time may lead to a break-up of the marriage. Every married couple, and those about to be married, should consult their physicians and obtain a clear picture of the mechanism of the sex act.''

Chapter 3

THE ART OF LOVE

"There is no gainsaying the fact that, although marriage is not wholly based on sexual attraction, and rightly it should not be, yet the question of sex in marriage is a most important one. Quite often the success or failure of a marriage depends on the knowledge that each of the partners has of sexual matters."

While there are a good many books dealing with sexual matters, most of them leave some points unclarified. What, then, are the mechanics of the sex act?

"Briefly, it consists of the introduction of the male organ into the female genital tract. Before this is accomplished, the penis must attain an erection from a relaxed, flaccid state. This is brought about by a reaction of the nervous mechanism of the entire body, initiated by sexual desire, which causes the male sex organ to become engorged with blood. This causes an erection and gives it the power of penetration."

But before penetration is accomplished is it not necessary that the woman be sexually aroused?

"Yes. That is the first prerequisite of a successful sex union. When only the male is ready and the female is still unaroused sexually, the sex act is doomed to failure. It should be realized that, before the sexual act is begun, a preliminary period of petting and fondling is required. During this preliminary play the clitoris, the vagina and the vulva become hyperemic, or blood-engorged, and sensitized. The clitoris becomes turgid and bends down to come in contact with the entering penis. As the penis enters the vagina, the various glands throw out a copious fluid which lubricates the entire vaginal tract, rendering the entrance of the penis much easier.''

After the preliminary play period, or petting, are both man and woman sufficiently aroused sexually for a more successful union?

"Yes, this is invariably true. After both the woman and the man are properly aroused, the sex act can be performed with greater enjoyment for both. With the woman's sexual emotion enhanced, the penis can gain entrance into the genital tract with greater ease, and while this is taking place, the vaginal muscles contract and adapt themselves to the entering organ. This increases the sensitiveness of the penis. The muscles of the womb also contract, opening up a small entrance to the womb in order to better receive the seminal fluid. Quite often the mouth of the womb comes in contact with the penis.

"During all this time the organs become more and more dilated with blood. This makes them harder and more sensitive. The glands of the female sex organs secrete a great deal of lubricating material and, with the continued friction to the movements of both parties, the acme of voluptuous sensation in both increases rapidly until a climax, called the orgasm, is reached.''

A great deal has been said about the orgasm. Just what is it?

''The orgasm is the very height of sexual feeling, and it corresponds with the violent ejaculation of fluid from various sexual glands. This climax generally takes place in the male somewhat earlier than in the female. In the male it takes place at the instant that the semen is ejaculated. In the female it takes place with the ejaculation of the various sexual secretions and the violent contractions of the genital muscles. During the act and especially at the orgasm, there is an increased rapidity in breathing and heart action, and finally, after the climax, there is a period of calm and relaxation.

''Until the orgasm is reached, the woman is in a state of continuous excitement, and immediately after the orgasm there is a feeling of satisfaction. Most women usually experience a feeling of sleepfulness and generally fall into a refreshing sleep.''

Is the first sexual union generally painful?

''Generally it is. But the discomfort is slight, consisting principally in the rupture of the hymen. Normally this is a rather thin membrane and rupture is accomplished with very little discomfort. However, it may be rather thick, and rupture during the act may cause pain. This difficulty may be overcome through physical examination by a physician. If the hymen is abnormally thick, it can be cut by the physician with a scalpel, with little discomfort. When this precaution is taken the first sexual union will be free from pain."

Is the hymen completely ruptured after sexual intercourse?

"If the act is properly performed it should be. However, there have been cases of partially ruptured hymen in women who were pregnant. This proves, of course, that pregnancy may actually take place even when the hymen is still partially present."

A great deal has been said about various positions to assume during the sex act. Do these positions contribute to the pleasure of the act?

"The question of the proper position to assume during sexual intercourse is one that always arouses a great deal of interest. Each couple has this problem to face, and in most instances it is an individual problem. What may be the proper position for one couple may be entirely out of the question for another."

Is there any particular position that can be generally recommended?

"This is like asking: Is there any particular book that will please all people, or any particular food that will prove the most popular. The question of positions is a highly personal one. You must experiment and find out for yourself. What may be suitable for you will not prove desirable for others, and vice versa.

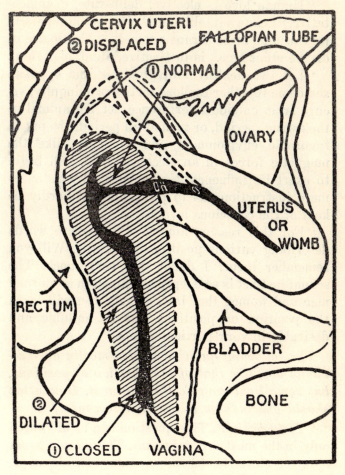

Average Life Size Vagina and Womb—Normal and Distended

This diagram, representing a cross-section through the center of the female body, from front to back, indicates the average life size of the vagina and uterus and, in dotted lines, the extent to which the vagina can be dilated or stretched by displacement of other organs. However, this is enormously increased under special conditions; those of childbirth open the expanded womb and vagina until they will pass the head of the baby.

"Human love is elective, deliberate, argumentative. It shows intelligent choice, no blindness in its train, no mere errant sensuality. Erotic ardor, on the other hand, is instinctive, blind, elemental.

"Let two healthy individuals of the opposite sex come together in close tactile propinquity, secure from outside interference, let the animal at the estrual period, or man at all periods, be put in favorable environment and sexuality, like the magnetic forces in an electrical field, will begin to exert its influence. Under such circumstances mere instructions as to positions will hardly be kept at the conscious level.

"For this reason, among others, mere words describing various positions are futile. Will you remember them? I doubt this very much. The sexual instinct is so deeply ingrained in all normal men and women that instinctively you will learn the position or positions that is suitable and desirable in your particular case."

The following question is also mostly an individual one, like that of the question of positions, but some light may be thrown on it. How often should one indulge in sexual intercourse?

"You are right. This question can be answered only in the most general terms. There are a great many factors to be taken into consideration. Health, age and the strength of the sex urge, all have to be considered.

"From time immemorial, philosopher and moralist have had definite ideas as to the length of time that should elapse between periods of sexual union. Socrates and Solon said that ten days was the required period. Zoroaster believed that nine days was a reasonable number. Mahomet prescribed eight days, Martin Luther advised twice a week. Moses forbade intercourse during menstruation, and for a week after the cessation of the flow.

"With the exception of Moses, all these worthy gentlemen were mistaken. You can't lay down specific regulations for such a complex problem.

"The highly sexed may indulge in coitus every night or perhaps even twice daily with no ill-effects. The moderately sexed will require sexual intercourse every other day, and will receive sufficient gratification. The undersexed may require coitus only once a week, or perhaps only once a month. In general, the frequency of sexual union depends upon the individuals, their health, sex urge and inclination."

Are there any factors which make for a more satisfactory consummation of the sex act?

"Yes, indeed. There are several very important factors, and each should receive very careful consideration. For instance, the time and place of the sex act is a very important consideration. Arrangements should be made whereby the early evening, and sometimes the late morning hours, or afternoons, on Sundays, for example, can be used for love-making.

"The bedroom should be removed from conditions which may tend to cause annoyance during the act. Utter privacy is required. Ringing doorbells and the fear of visitors tend to disrupt the act and its pleasurable consummation.

"Cleanliness is another essential for the proper enjoyment of the sex act. A visit to the bathroom and dressing table should always precede intercourse. A thorough bath is one of the best means of insuring desire. The woman may use perfumes which are particularly alluring. There is a very intimate relationship between pleasant odors and increased sexual desire.

"There is no doubt that the five special senses: sight, hearing, smell, touch and taste enter very significantly into the enjoyment of sexual intercourse. In the Orient there are special perfumes which are said to augment sexual desire. It has been found that in women the love for musk and similar perfumes is related to sexual excitement.

"The sense of sight is also very important. That is why undress is a requirement. Clothes do not act as an inducement. A clean and healthy body does."

Now, what are some of the hygienic aspects of the sex act?

"Every act of sexual union has a profound influence on the nervous system. There is a marked increase in the action of the heart. The circulation of the blood is accelerated. Every organ in the body is affected.

"When the sex act is carried out normally and at reasonable intervals of time, no ill-effects result. Unfortunately, there is still no widespread knowledge of sexual hygiene.

"For instance, excessive sexual intercourse acts as a constant stimulant to the nervous system, and will in time result in nervous irritability.

Coitus interruptus, in which the husband breaks off the act of intercourse without waiting for his wife to reach her orgasm, acts as a distinct shock to his wife's nervous system.

"In women who practice *coitus reservatus,* forbidding the orgasm to take place by will-power, for any length of time, are palpitation of the heart and marked nervous upsets quite likely to result. Among the most common are sensations of faintness, headaches, attacks of dizziness, weakness and a general feeling of utter misery. Some women later become depressed, having weeping spells, digestive upsets and nervous prostration."

Are all women capable of enjoying the sex act?

"Unfortunately not. In some cases there may be something wrong with a woman's sexual organs which may prevent normal enjoyment of the act. She may be otherwise entirely normal, and yet there may be a slight abnormality which will render it impossible for her to attain sexual satisfaction."

What brings this about?

"Several factors may be found to be responsible. But before they are discussed, first note that the name *dyspareunia* is given to pain and discomfort experienced by a woman during sexual intercourse.

"*Dyspareunia* must be distinguished from two somewhat similar disorders: *vaginismus* and *anesthesia sexualis.* In *vaginismus* the introduction of a foreign body into the vagina gives rise to painful spasms there. This renders sexual intercourse impossible or difficult. Sexual anes-

thesia means just what the name implies, a complete absence of sexual feeling. *Dyspareunia*
means an experiencing of pain during the sexual
act.

"There are many cases of *dyspareunia*. These
may be generally divided into nervous causes and
local causes. A thorough examination is required
to bring the precise causes to light, so that they
may be treated and corrected."

Is dyspareunia *a rare condition? Does it have
any appreciable effect if not corrected?*

"*Dyspareunia* is not a very rare condition. It
is the cause of much marital unhappiness. Certainly it has a profound effect on a woman's
entire existence. The thought of being deprived
of sexual love often produces a deep emotional
depression which will in time develop hypochon-
dria or melancholia with its many unpleasant
by-products. Hysteria and neurasthenia are also
produced by this disorder."

*Does painful sexual feeling in women produce
any physical disorder?*

"Yes, and these physical disorders are quite
marked. The constant flooding of the genital
organs with blood results in a chronic stasis, or
arrest of the blood current, which leads in time
to a state of chronic inflammation. Other more
serious results are disorders of menstruation, and
bleeding from the womb. The formation of tumors
has a possible origin in this trouble.

"Remember that pregnancy and a new life
begin with the fertilization of the female ovum
by the male spermatozoön. This is the biological

end-result of love between a man and a woman.
Pregnancy and prenatal hygiene are topics of
great importance, and these will be the next
consideration."

Chapter 4

PRENATAL CARE AND HYGIENE

After conception has taken place and pregnancy is definitely established are there any hygienic measures that can be adopted to make pregnancy safer?

"There are quite a few of them. Modern medical science has contributed a great deal to the management of pregnancy. Prenatal care very often determines the success or failure of what will take place in the delivery room in a few months.

"No detail is overlooked. Consider, for example, such a common phenomenon as morning sickness or nausea. This is one of the symptoms of pregnancy and, to many women, these periodic attacks of nausea are very disagreeable. Formerly nothing very much was done about this condition. But now a great deal can be done to alleviate these morning spells."

What are the precautions a woman suffering from these attacks should take?

"She should rest in bed for a day and restrict the diet to dry toast or crackers and weak hot tea. The bowels should be opened with a mild laxative if necessary. Intercourse should be taboo. On succeeding mornings she should take a light breakfast of tea and toast half an hour before rising.

"This plan, if followed for several days, may prevent a recurrence of the nausea. If such simple measures fail, more radical steps may have to be employed. The modern medical treatment consists of rest in bed, dietary considerations, sedative medicines and glandular extracts. These extracts are derived from the pituitary and ovary glands and are usually very effective.

"Not so many years ago, physicians often met with cases of vomiting in which all available remedies were ineffective, so that surgical abortion had to be used, thus terminating pregnancy. Under modern methods of treatment, this is seldom necessary. There are less drastic measures which may be employed with considerable success."

Doesn't pregnancy put a strain on vital organs, like the kidneys and the heart?

"Often it does. As a matter of fact, one of the most alarming complications of pregnancy is functional failure of the kidneys. Ordinarily, all the vital organs have a functional capacity considerably in excess of the ordinary needs of the body in the maintenance of health. But some of these organs may be overworked and damaged, so that disagreeable symptoms occur. If, at any time, they have been damaged by disease or excesses, the danger of overworking them becomes greater. For instance, if one has had acute rheumatism, the heart may become damaged so that violent exercise later on may result in serious consequences.

"Likewise, the stomach and liver may be harmed permanently by the continual use of alcoholic beverages, so that these organs become more subject to disease or derangement as a result of overeating or overdrinking. The kidneys are often damaged during childhood by certain infections, particularly scarlet fever. If they have been hurt in this way, or if they have little reserve capacity, the extra work they have to do during pregnancy in excreting or throwing off the waste products of mother and child may be too heavy a load for them to carry, so that symptoms of insufficiency develop.

"Symptoms of kidney dysfunction, or lack of proper functioning, are apt to be brought on or aggravated if there is a further increase in the waste material to be excreted because of hard work or violent exercise, or if the excretory functions of the skin and bowels are interfered with. This may happen if one drinks an insufficient amount of water or becomes constipated. Chilling of the skin by exposure or by wearing an insufficient amount of clothing may interfere with the normal invisible perspiration enough to overwork the kidneys and cause them to break down under this extra load. For this reason, the expectant mother should always dress warmly enough so that there will not be any possibility of becoming chilled at any time. Also, since hard work or violent exercise increases the amount of waste matter to be thrown off by the kidneys, such excesses should be avoided. The expectant mother should have a well-balanced diet—just sufficient for her needs. She should drink an adequate, but not excessive, amount of water, and no alcoholic beverages, and secure more rest and sleep than is ordinarily required.''

What are the signs of kidney failure during pregnancy?

''The earliest signs of kidney trouble may be detected and later more serious complications avoided. Among these signs are a slight swelling of the ankles, which is present in the morning as well as in the evening. Such swelling of the ankles may result from less serious causes, but it usually subsides after the patient rests in bed.

''There may be swelling of the hands and even of the face—particularly noticeable about the eyes. Headaches and, in the more serious cases, disturbances of vision may occur. The urine is apt to be scanty and highly colored, and may be slightly cloudy in appearance.

''If any of these signs are noticed, no matter if one feels perfectly well, kidney trouble should be suspected. Sudden attacks of kidney disease are quite possible. Even a slight cold may bring about such an attack.''

How are these attacks of kidney disorders treated?

''It all depends upon the nature of the kidney ailment. If it is severe, hospital care is required. Lighter attacks may be coped with by complete rest in bed, keeping the body at a uniformly warm temperature so as to promote perspiration, and encouraging free movement of the bowels.''

Aren't abortions a problem during the prenatal period?

"The problem of abortions is a most important one. Criminal abortions will not be discussed. It is estimated that 80,000 of these are performed annually in New York City alone, and about one million in the country as a whole. There are two kinds of abortions, those that are induced by surgical or medical means, and spontaneous abortions, which occur by themselves. Induced abortions may be legal or criminal. They are legal when performed by a reputable physician, in a reputable hospital, in order to save the mother's life. They are criminal when performed by some shady practitioner in his own office for no other reason than to cover up unsocial conduct.

"It is with spontaneous abortion that we shall concern ourselves. There is a considerable number of mothers who abort spontaneously one or more times. That is, their abortions are not induced by anyone, but are brought on by abnormal conditions in the mothers themselves. Among the causes which may disrupt the first, as well as later, pregnancies are irritable womb, spasmodic conditions, such as severe coughing and vomiting, severe general infections, and certain abnormal glandular conditions. Women who have had children, or have suffered abortions or venereal diseases, may abort because of chronic inflammatory conditions of the womb.

"The woman with an irritable womb may abort as a result of severe attacks of vomiting or coughing, sudden fright, extraction of teeth, sexual intercourse, severe purgation, a fall, sea-sickness, or over-exertion. Repeated abortions may be due to a very nervous disposition, thyroid disease, syphilis or habit. In those cases which seem to be due to nervousness, toxic goitre should be suspected. In other cases of unknown origin, the blood is examined for syphilis, regardless of how morally cleanly the husband and wife have lived, for syphilis may be contracted in an innocent manner.''

What are the signs of threatened abortion?

''The signs of threatened abortion are similar, in some instances, to those at the beginning of menstruation. If, for ten days or more, a woman passes the expected time for her menstruation, and then or later begins to have cramps, back-ache, a feeling of heaviness or bearing down, or symptoms of beginning menstruation, she should go to bed immediately and call her physician.

''If mild or severe hemorrhage begins, with the formation of blood clots, the diagnosis of beginning abortion is practically certain. If the physician is called before hemorrhage begins, very often he will be able to check these early symptoms by means of sedatives, so that pregnancy will go on to term, or normal. If he is not called until considerable bleeding has taken place, and the uterine contractions or cramps have resulted in considerable dilatation of the mouth of the womb, he can do very little, as a rule, to prevent the abortion. For this reason, it is imperative that newly married couples should keep these facts in mind, since few of them realize what these symptoms signify until it is too late."

Does spontaneous abortion become habitual if care is not taken to prevent it?

"Yes, abortions sometimes become habitual following one or more spontaneous, self-induced or criminal abortions. A woman who has aborted at the third month of pregnancy, for instance, naturally or otherwise, is more apt to abort again spontaneously at the same time period of pregnancy than one who has never aborted. Therefore it is imperative that any abortion be prevented if possible.

"Those who practice criminal abortion in order to postpone the bearing of children until a more convenient time, may find to their sorrow that, when they do wish to have children, it will be impossible."

Is it possible to postpone an abortion until the later months of pregnancy so as to give the new-born child a better chance to live?

"Sometimes abortions can be postponed, by appropriate treatment, until the last few months of pregnancy. When this is the case, we have what is called a premature birth. If such births occur at the seventh month or later, the baby may survive.

"There is a common belief that a premature baby at seven months has a better chance to live than one at eight months. No grounds exist for this belief. The nearer the pregnancy approaches to full term, the greater the prospect for the survival of the baby."

What are the precautions a pregnant woman should take to avoid complications?

"The pregnant woman should lead a rather quiet, protected life if she would guard her own health and the life of her child. Her life should be free from any great excitement, and she should avoid extremes of heat and cold. She should not take long journeys. In this connection, it should be remembered that during disease epidemics, there is a greater danger of contagion while traveling than while remaining at home.

"While walking, sea bathing, riding and traveling are permissible during the first half of pregnancy, provided that the patient is in normal health, violent exercise at any time is not advisable. The over-exertion, excitement and minor accidents incident to sports and traveling, which have no significance at other times, may have grave consequences in bringing about some of the serious complications of pregnancy. The best open-air exercises for pregnant women are walking and driving, and these should be enjoyed throughout pregnancy. The woman who shuts herself in and takes little or no out-of-door exercise during the latter part of pregnancy, may expect to have a more disagreeable time at childbirth than she who makes it a practice to take open-air exercise every day."

What about sex relations during pregnancy?

"In many women, pregnancy, particularly during its early part, has no effect upon the libido, or love life, and, in women who are normal and healthy, intercourse may be permitted during the first half of pregnancy. It must be remembered, however, that many cases of nausea and threatened abortion have been brought about or aggravated by it. Therefore it should be taboo for women who have been threatened with abortion and in those subject to nausea. It should also be avoided by pregnant women if it is disagreeable or painful, no matter how healthy they may be."

Are there any special dietary precautions that must be taken during the prenatal period?

"The diet during this time should be a well-balanced one of meat, cereals, vegetables and fruits. The tendency toward a perversion of taste and appetite must be resisted, and a wholesome mixed diet should be followed. Some women jeopardize their own health and that of their unborn child by limiting their diet to certain articles of food, so that some of the necessary elements and vitamins are denied them.

"Those who have voracious appetites should hold them in check, since overeating overworks the kidneys and results in the deposit of undesirable fat. It may also result in excessive size of the baby, so that labor will be more difficult than it should be. Plenty of fruits and leafy vegetables should be eaten, not only for their laxative effect but for their vitamin content.

"Women who are not exposed to a great deal of sunshine out-of-doors should take a liberal amount of cod-liver oil daily. One of the newer concentrates containing equal values in vitamins A and D is permissible and more palatable than cod-liver oil. Vitamin D is necessary for the normal development of the bones and teeth of the child. In addition, vitamin D and calcium are essential to the health of the mother.

"Pregnancy is a severe strain upon the calcium supply of the mother, and may result in softening of the structure of her bones, as well as interfering with the coagulability of her blood, so that hemorrhage at the time of childbirth is more liable to occur and may be difficult to control. An adequate supply of vitamin D in the form of cod-liver oil will eliminate this danger. If, in addition to cod-liver oil, the expectant mother will take a teaspoonful of calcium gluconate or a tablet of discalcium phosphate twice daily during the latter months of pregnancy, this will be an added precaution against hemorrhage and will protect her teeth against undue decay."

What about beverages?

"The expectant mother should drink water freely. Milk is a very desirable food, and may also be taken in liberal quantities. Alcoholic beverages should be avoided entirely. The popular fallacy that beer is a valuable and desirable food, and is a useful addition to the diet of pregnant women, is not worthy of credence. To be sure malt and brewer's yeast have important vitamin values, but these are either destroyed or so greatly diluted in the brewing process that their value in beer becomes insignificant."

With women smoking now more than they ever did before, should smoking be prohibited during pregnancy?

"Tobacco, like alcohol, should be avoided during pregnancy and lactation, or the nursing period. The reason is that tobacco is absorbed by the same blood that nourishes the growing child in the womb. If the blood is not entirely pure and free from toxic elements the future health of the unborn child will be adversely affected.

"Dr. F. W. Peterson, an obstetrician of great experience, has made the following very interesting statements: 'In my own personal experience I have never seen any mother who was an habitual smoker go through the ordeals of pregnancy and delivery as uniformly successfully as those who did not use tobacco. Nor have I seen any children of these mothers as physically and mentally fit to meet the emergencies of life as the children of mothers who used no tobacco. With this constantly growing use of the weed by the mothers of the land, we stand fair to produce eventually a generation of neurotics.'

"These are rather startling statements to make, yet science bears out Dr. Peterson in his conclusions. The reason why tobacco exerts this unhealthy influence upon the unborn child and the nursing infant is that the circulation in the womb and the breasts of the mother is interferred with.

"Cigarette-smoking mothers do not stand pregnancy or childbirth as well as those who do not smoke, because their general nutrition is interfered with. As mentioned above, the blood absorbs a certain amount of nicotine and other toxic elements from the tobacco. With the added strain of pregnancy, these poisonous materials exert all the greater damage on the heart and kidneys. It is therefore a very good idea for a woman to abstain from tobacco during pregnancy and the nursing period.

"Pregnancy is a very important period in every married woman's life. A number of problems related to it will be discussed, among them being the tests for pregnancy, changes taking place during pregnancy, and the stages of childbirth."

Chapter 5

SOME PERTINENT FACTS ABOUT
PREGNANCY

"The ultimate object of marriage and marital relations is the attainment of parenthood. Having children is the biological urge back of a man and woman living together as husband and wife. When the male sex cell unites with the female sex cell, fertilization occurs and the first step toward having a child has been made. In time, this results in pregnancy."

Are there any tests for pregnancy that will remove any doubt from a woman's mind that she is pregnant?

"Yes, there is a very widely used test, invented by two German doctors, Aschheim and Zondek, known popularly as the A-Z Test. It is purely biological, depending upon the fact that during pregnancy certain hormones of the pituitary glands are secreted in the blood and are present in the urine. When a small quantity of urine is injected into a female mouse or rabbit, certain changes in the ovaries of the animal are brought about within from one to five days, if the woman from whom the urine was taken was pregnant. If she was not pregnant, these changes do not take place in the injected animal."

Is this test absolutely reliable?

"It is accurate in about 98 per cent of cases, and is the most reliable test for pregnancy that we now have. X-ray is still more reliable, but it cannot be applied in the very early months as the A-Z test can. X-ray reveals the presence of the fetus only when its bones are sufficiently developed to show on the X-ray plate, and this is possible only after the pregnancy is rather far advanced."

Are there any definite clear-cut symptoms that a woman experiences when she is definitely pregnant?

"There are certain classical or standard symptoms which are quite typical and characteristic of pregnancy. First, there is a cessation of the monthly periods. Within a month after conception has taken place, the woman may begin to have attacks of nausea in the morning. There are typical changes in the breast; they begin to enlarge and the color in the area around the nipples deepens. As pregnancy goes on, the womb increases in size and there is a protuberance of the abdomen.

" 'Quickening,' or movement of the child, may be felt at about the fourth month, as a rule. At first these movements appear as a faint fluttering, but in a short time they become more definite. Later in pregnancy they become decidedly disagreeable. Occasionally, the mother may not feel life until the seventh month, or possibly a little later, but generally it is much earlier than that.

"Other symptoms of pregnancy are changes in

the woman's disposition and appetite, perversion of taste, sour stomach or heartburn, pigmented spots on the skin of the face, and either lessened or increased action of the bowels. Women who are subject to varicose veins of the legs will notice that they begin to swell soon after pregnancy begins.''

What is the duration of pregnancy?

''The average duration of pregnancy is two hundred and seventy-one days, but this may vary considerably within normal limits. Since pregnancy usually begins on the tenth to the thirteenth day following the beginning of menstruation, it is customary to figure about two hundred and eighty days from the beginning of menstruation. A simple way to compute this, is to count back three months from the first day of the last menstruation and add seven days.''

Is it possible for a mother to influence her child while she is carrying it in her womb?

''A great deal has been written on the subject of prenatal influence. Most of it is utter nonsense. External conditions, such as the mother's seeing a hump-back, being frightened by a dog, or witnessing a terrible accident will not affect the unborn child mentally or physically. The child's mental and physical characteristics have already been imparted to it by the chromosomes in the father's and mother's sex cells. No outside influences will alter them.''

What are the signs that a woman is going into labor?

''There are definite signs that labor is begin-

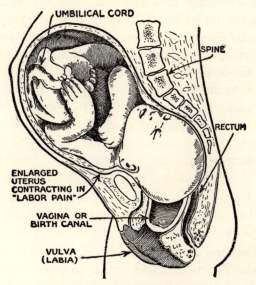

A fully-developed foetus, or unborn child, is
about to be delivered from the womb.

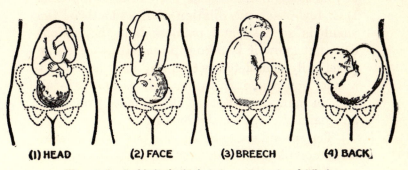

(1) HEAD   (2) FACE   (3) BREECH   (4) BACK

"Presentations" of baby for birth, in increasing order of difficulty.

ning. She may be warned by the appearance of one or more of the following signs or symptoms:

1. A feeling of heaviness or bearing down.
2. Intermittent pressure symptoms or pains in the lower part of the back.
3. Intermittent cramps or pains in the abdomen, from five minutes to one hour apart.
4. The expulsion of a small amount of bloody mucus, commonly called the show.
5. A gush of water indicating the breaking of the protective bag of water that surrounds the child.''

What about the actual process of childbirth itself? What does it consist of?

''The process of childbirth is divided into three stages. The first begins with the onset of labor and lasts until the mouth of the womb is fully dilated. There is a great variation in the duration of this stage, and in the severity of its symptoms. In a few cases the dilation of the mouth of the womb is so easy and painless that the patient does not know it is taking place. It may even be practically completed before any pain is felt. As a rule, however, it is rather tedious and painful, and, in many instances, it is the most prolonged and painful stage of childbirth.

''The second stage of labor is that in which the child completes its descent through the pelvic canal of the mother, and is born. At the beginning of labor, the child's head or other presenting part has, as a rule, begun to pass from the abdominal cavity to the pelvic cavity. It is said to be engaged. During the stage while the mouth of the womb is being dilated, the child presses still lower into this cavity. Sometimes it advances so rapidly that as soon as the cervix or constricted part of the womb is fully dilated, only a few contractions are required to complete the birth. Usually, however, considerable expulsive force is required.

"The duration of this stage, the suffering to be endured, and the assistance required before the child can be born, depend upon several factors. Some of these are referable to the child and some to the mother. The size of the child, the size of the bony outlet, and the force of the uterine contractions are the main factors.

"The third stage of labor is that in which the placenta, or after-birth, is delivered. As soon as the baby is born, the physician exerts firm pressure on the womb through the abdominal wall. Thus an effort is made to prevent hemorrhage and cause the womb to expel the placenta. After the placenta is expelled, labor comes to an end.

"Once the child is born, the placenta delivered, and hemorrhage checked, the mother should be fitted with a snug abdominal binder. There are several reasons for this. It makes the patient more comfortable, and, by firm pressure over the womb, aids in the prevention of after-labor bleeding."

How soon after the birth of the child should a couple wait before resuming marital relations?

"Under ordinary conditions it is best to wait for at least six weeks before resuming sexual relations. During this time certain changes are taking place in the internal sex organs of the woman, and there are discharges, or lochias. Sexual relations during this time interfere with the natural regenerative processes.''

Can pregnancy be controlled?

''Yes. There are several methods. The first is to abstain from sexual intercourse. The second is to employ certain mechanical and chemical contraceptives, and the third is to take advantage of the so-called 'safe-period.' ''

Is it possible for normally sexed people to refrain, or remain continent for any length of time?

''It would not seem so, and, for this reason the theory of abstaining from sexual intercourse to prevent pregnancy is not very practical.''

What about the so-called safe-period?

''Through a series of very careful studies, Ogino and Knaus have been able to determine very definitely the exact period in the menstrual cycle of women, during which time they are fertile and may conceive. Before the findings of these two men were published, it was generally believed that the most fertile period in women was in the days immediately following menstruation, although there was no scientific basis for this belief.

''Ogino and Knaus found that ovulation, or the casting off of the ovum from the ovary, took place exactly fifteen days prior to the first day of menstruation and that a woman was fertile only three days prior to ovulation and one day thereafter. These findings were later verified by American doctors.''

Woman's Calendar of Sex—The Monthly Cycle

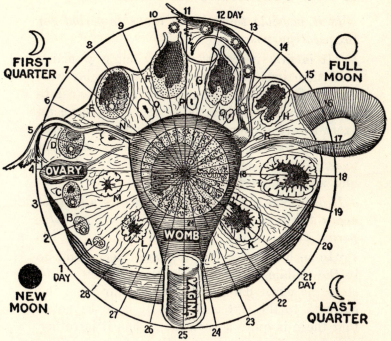

Woman's sex organs (fetus indicated, in the womb) with an ovary highly magnified in the background. The successive daily stages of an ovum are shown from A to F, when it has entered the Fallopian tube and, if it is fertilized here, pregnancy results. The letters from G to R show the change of the follicle to corpus luteum, its growth and final shrinkage. In case of pregnancy, its hormones prevent further production of ova and, therefore, menstruation.

Women's Menstrual Cycle and Married Life

	1	2	3	4	5	6	7	8	9	10	11	12	13	14	15	16	17	18	19	20	21	22	23	24	25	26	27	28	NEW CYCLE BEGINS
BIOLOGICAL	M	M	M	M	M	M	M	I	I	I	I	I	I	I	I	I	I	I	I	I	I	I	I	I	I	I	I	I	M
JEWISH	M	M	M	M	M	M	M	C	C	C	C	C	C	I	I	I	I	I	I	I	I	I	I	I	I	I	I	I	I
OGINO-KNAUS	M	M	M	M	M	M	M	S	S	S	F	F	F	F	F	F	F	F	S	S	S	S	S	S	S	S	S	S	M

MENSTRUATION	STERILE	OVULATION FERTILE	STERILE

C CONTINENCE   I INTERCOURSE

The figures represent days of a normal 28-day menstrual cycle, and presumed marital relations during them: (1) biological, or natural, intercourse permitted except during menstruation; (2) Jewish or Mosaic code, with seven days' separation after menses; (3) Ogino-Knaus rule for sterile (or "safe") and fertile intercourse.

Is it possible to estimate the safe-period for practical purposes?

"It is first necessary to find out a woman's ovulation time, and this varies considerably with her monthly periods. In order to be able to establish the safe-period, it is necessary to have an exact record of her monthly periods for at least a year. From this it is next necessary carefully to chart her individual cycles in order to get some idea as to ovulation time."

If a woman regularly has her monthly periods every twenty-eight days, what would her safe-period be?

"In such a case her ovulation period would be in the middle of the month. It is impossible to state the exact date, which may occur from the eleventh to the sixteenth day. It is to be noted that there is quite a variation. Thus it is rather unsafe to rely upon the so-called safe-period. The fact is that very few women have regular monthly periods. Most of them have irregular periods, and this makes the calculation of the so-called safe-period very difficult."

Do you think that one may safely rely upon the safe-period to prevent pregnancy?

"From a long experience of observation in this matter, it may be said no faith can be placed in the so-called safe-period."

Then the only other safe, practical method is the use of contraceptives?

"Yes. The use of contraceptives by the man and the woman is a practical way of preventing pregnancy. Contraceptives are mechanical and chemical agencies employed either to destroy the male elements of conception or to prevent their entry into the womb. They consist of various antiseptic preparations, including suppositories, jellies and powders, and rubber appliances. There are now many Birth-control clinics throughout the United States which give practical instructions in the use of contraceptives."

How often should a woman bear children?

"There are various factors to be considered. First, there is the health of the woman. Too frequent childbearing will wear out even the hardiest of women. Childbirths should be spaced at least two or three years apart. Perhaps longer intervals are more desirable in some cases.

"Economics also enters into the question. Women who have no means of providing for their children should not have too many of them. This is easier said than done, and it is here that the birth-control clinics are doing such marvelous work."

What is the length of the active childbearing period of a woman?

"It is about thirty years, beginning at puberty, when the menstrual periods start, and ending at the menopause, when they cease."

Are there any instances of women bearing children after the age of 45?

"There are quite a few authentic instances of pregnancy occurring during middle age, and even in old age. Dr. E. Lorand tells of the case of an Italian woman of 69 who was still attractive and good-looking at that age, and who looked not more than 45. She had had 12 children, and had not yet reached her menopause. Dr. Lorand assumed that she was capable of having children even at 70.

"Not so long ago an interesting case was reported in the newspapers. In Valladoid, Spain, Mrs. Pedro Lorenzo, at the age of 68, became the mother of her 29th child. There are several other cases of childbirth at advanced ages. Katherine, Countess of Desmond, was reputed to have lived 140 years, and to have had a daughter after she was 65. An English couple, Benjamin and Elizabeth Atkins lived together fruitfully for a great many years. In official French archives is reported the case of La Belle Paule Fiesche, of Rue de la Perle, Paris, who became a mother at the age of 90. The child, a boy, was born on December 1, 1742.

"Another very interesting case was that of Margaret Krasionwana of the village of Konin, Poland, who died in 1763 at the age of 108. At the age of 94 she married her third husband, Kasper Raycol, aged 105. During the fourteen years they lived together, she bore him two boys and a girl."

How about the other extreme? Can children be born at very early ages?

"Yes. Cases have been reported of children of five, six, seven and eight years of age becoming pregnant and giving birth to normal babies. Only recently, the case of a five-year-old mother was reported in Brazil. In southern countries the menses starts much earlier than in the more northern climates. Thus it is possible for child-birth to occur at a very early age."

Those answers are very interesting side-lights on pregnancy, but to return to normal pregnancy, are there any special rules of health and hygiene that should be followed after childbirth?

"There certainly are. One of the most frequent changes that occur after childbirth is the tendency to put on weight. Dr. C. Barborka and other nutritional experts have pointed out that during and following pregnancy there is an increased demand for food, which, when not regulated, will often result in obesity.

"A gradual gain in weight, amounting to a total of sixteen to twenty pounds above normal in the last month, is to be expected. An increase markedly greater than this is not normal. Provided that the mother was undernourished preceding pregnancy, a gain of thirty or more pounds is not to be viewed with complacency. Careful regulation of eating habits is called for after childbirth.

"Carbohydrates produce energy and also maintain and build up the glycogen reserve. During pregnancy the body uses up more carbohydrates than normally. While there may be an increase in carbohydrate foods during the childbearing period, following childbirth this type of food is best restricted."

What about fat-containing foods?

"These foods are also increased during pregnancy. Some physicians have placed the daily allotment of fat at 100 grams. The amount may vary above or below this quantity, according to whether the patient is overweight or underweight. During pregnancy, about 80 grams of fat daily may be permitted, but this quantity must be reduced considerably after the birth of the child.''

What about the third class of foods, protein-containing elements?

"During pregnancy, a protein intake of 2 grams per kilogram of body weight has been suggested. This is double the normal requirement, but extra protein is needed for the growth of the unborn child. However, following childbirth this should be cut in half.''

Are there any other hygienic measures which should be observed during the post-partum, or after childbirth, period?

"Yes. During the latter months of pregnancy a woman generally restricts her physical activities, and these should now be resumed. She can indulge in light sports, such as tennis, in order to strengthen her abdominal muscles, which have been weakened during child-birth. Walking, swimming and other forms of activity which bring muscles into play is desirable to reactivate the circulation of the blood and revitalize the tissues. This will prove very gratifying, as pregnancy is a confining period during which there is a slowing up of bodily activity.

"During lactation, or the nursing period, the production of milk becomes a matter for consideration. The mother must include in her dietary those foods which will supply the constituents that go into the making of an adequate milk supply. Particularly is vitamin D required. One quart of milk is an absolute necessity. It has been found that whole-grain cereals add to the mineral content of the diet. This is especially important because the danger of rickets is of the greatest concern during the first few months of the infant's life.

"Meat, fish and chicken are other articles of food of prime importance during lactation. They supply sufficient protein, fat and minerals in varying amounts. Muscle meat is a good source of iron and of vitamin G, while glandular organs contain vitamins A and B. Both meat and fish are high in phosphorus, which is so essential in promoting strong bones and teeth.

"The meals may follow the routine to which the nursing mother is accustomed, provided that all the foods necessary to fulfill the requirements are taken. During the period of lactation the child is given its first real start in life. If that start is a fairly good one, the child will develop into a normal, healthy human being.

"A good many factors in a successful marriage have now been discussed. There are, however, a good many more, and to a discussion of these we will now proceed."

PART II

OVERCOMING SEXUAL DIFFICULTIES

Chapter 6

ORGANIC IMPOTENCE CAN BE OVERCOME

Impotence is perhaps the most common sexual difficulty met with in men. It is a disability, with many ramifications in the organic and psychic makeup of the individual. Among the most frequently asked questions are those relating to impotence. Following is a compendium of the commonest questions raised and the answers that modern medicine is able to give.

A great deal has been said about impotence— just what is this condition?

"Impotence means the inability to perform the sex act."

Is impotence the same in all cases?

"No. In general, there are two forms of impotence: organic and psychic. Organic impotence signifies a type of sexual disability which is caused by some physical condition in the body. Psychic impotence is a somewhat more difficult problem. It refers to impotence which is caused by some mental or emotional disorder."

Is not organic impotence caused actually by some definitely physical upset?

"Yes, this type of impotence refers to physical disorders which interfere with the erection of the

penis or the duration of the sex act on the part
of the male. In all other respects he may be
entirely normal, and yet his sexual power may be
below normal. This loss of sexual strength may
come on with dramatic suddenness, but more frequently it comes on gradually."

Just what causes organic impotence?

"There are quite a few causes. Any disease
which affects the genital organs may bring about
impotence. Gonorrhea and syphilis have played
an important role in causing it. Inflammatory
conditions of the internal sexual organs, such as
inflammation of the seminal vesicles in which
seminal fluid is stored, will quite often result in
a loss of sexual power. Diseases of the prostate
gland often result in impotence, particularly
when it becomes enlarged.

"When the glandular secretion of the internal
sex glands is interfered with, impotence may
often result. Tumors and growths in the region
of the sexual organs also have a harmful effect
on the ability to perform the sex act. Still another fertile cause of physical or organic impotence is a diseased nerve supply to the sex
organs. The too frequent and too excessive use
of drugs, narcotics and alcohol will also bring
about a loss of sexual power.

"There are also a number of transitory causes
of physical impotence caused by easily corrected
conditions. Among the most frequent of these
are: general fatigue, abnormal sex practices,
disproportion of the male or female sex organs,
improper lubrication of the female sex organs

during the act, and a very thick, resistant hymen. These are not so very difficult to overcome. A little common sense will often solve the problem."

What would you say is the most common abnormal sex act which causes organic impotence?

"*Coitus interruptus.* This act involves the withdrawal of the penis from the vagina before ejaculation has occurred. This is a very common practice and a harmful one. Many men who practice it think that it is harmless. But this is far from the truth. This practice will often bring about an inflammation of the internal sex organs such as the seminal vesicles, for example, and this will lead to inability to perform the act.

"The loss of an important function of the body may often be traced to a serious condition elsewhere. Low blood pressure, for example, may result in weak erections and the inability to perform the act. Serious ailments of the heart, the kidneys and the blood-forming organs also exact their toll."

How is this type of organic impotence treated?

"By removing its direct and immediate cause. If the cause is due to abnormal sex practices they must be stopped. If the cause is due to the use of drugs or alcohol, these must be promptly discontinued. Tumors or other growths should be removed, and quite often following such an operation the direct cause of the impotence will disappear and the man will be restored to sexual efficiency.

"Medical ailments, such as low blood pressure, diseases of the heart and kidneys and of the blood-forming organs require very careful and persistent treatment. Low blood pressure may be raised by the use of various drugs and physical therapy. Diseases of the heart, kidney and blood-forming organs are quite amenable to treatment. In a considerable number of instances when there is a perceptible improvement in the underlying condition, the ability to perform the marital act will increase."

Is there not a type of organic impotence due to poor development of the male sex organs?

"Yes, and unfortunately, this is quite a common cause of physical impotence. The failure of the male sex organs to develop is due to a failure of the internal ductless glands to secrete the fluids necessary for the development of the sex organs, particularly of the penis."

Can anything be done about this type of impotence?

"Fortunately, science has developed to such a point within the last few years that a great deal can be done. The active principle of the internal sex secretions has recently been isolated in pure form. This preparation can be given to impotent men, with gratifying results. The name of this active principle is *testosterone propionate*.

"A man with arrested development of his sexual organs due to lack of internal secretion of this important hormone, presents a typical picture. First, his sex organs retain a small infantile size (as well as appearance) and this, of course, is the direct cause of his impotence.

His voice is thin and high-pitched; his skin is dry and lusterless; and the growth of hair on his face and other parts of his body is scant. His prostate is also small, and it contains little or no fluid. He lacks energy and initiative.

"This type of organic impotence has claimed the attention of science, and a great deal has been accomplished in overcoming it. There are two methods of treatment. One consists of injecting *testosterone propionate* in oil in sufficiently large quantities, 25 milligrams, at least, every day. Many physicians who are a bit too timid, and who do not inject a sufficient dose, will fail to get results. The body is lacking in this very essential male hormone and it must be supplied in sizable quantities.

"Within two weeks, with proper treatment, results begin to manifest themselves. There is the beginning of erectile strength, which at first is not very marked. Also, there is an increase in muscular strength in other parts of the body. The hair, too, increases in growth, and the voice acquires added power and timber.

"Within about six weeks the penis begins to increase in strength, and erection is by now definitely possible. This means that there has been a one hundred percent increase in sexual power. By now the organic impotence can be said to have been overcome. There is also a further increase in muscular strength. The hair is now more profuse and stiffer in growth. The voice is definitely of a masculine pitch and the emotional and psychic makeup is also more that of a virile man's rather than that of a sexless nonentity.

"Lately, a more advanced and more effective form of treatment has been devised in treating organic impotence due to infantilism of the sex organs. Pellets made from the crystalline *testosterone propionate* are used instead of *testosterone* in oil.

"The method of implanting these pellets is simple and painless. A wheal is made in the skin of the thigh with a solution of nupercaine. The instrument, with the pellets of *testosterone* inside, is pushed painlessly through the skin and the pellets are deposited in the muscle of the thigh. A silver clip is then used to close the puncture wound.

"Usually three such pellets are implanted at a time, and the results are almost immediate. Quite often after the third day following such an implantation of *testosterone,* the man is capable of having an erection. In time this increases in strength and duration. This instrument and method of treatment was devised by Drs. Samuel A. Vest and John E. Howard, who have used it with excellent results in a large series of cases.

"As the treatment is continued, the penis increases in size and the voice deepens. There is also an increase in the density of hair growth.

"The physical causes of impotence can be seen, felt and measured and for this reason do not present very great difficulties in treatment. However, the second type of impotence, psychic impotence, is quite another matter."

Chapter 7

THE MANAGEMENT OF PSYCHIC IMPOTENCE

Are the causes of psychic impotence different from those of organic?

"They most certainly are, and they are also more difficult to treat. Quite often they require the services of a psychiatrist or psychoanalyst.

"Let us consider the main causes of psychic impotence.

1. Lack of love for the partner is very often a cause. If a man does not love his wife, he quite often loses his desire for her. Yet he may be sexually potent with another woman.

2. Extreme anxiety and fear will often act as a deterrent to the sex act. Fear of infection or fear of the wife's becoming pregnant has been known to destroy sexual desire.

3. Fear of the consequences of excessive masturbation will often so prey on a man's mind that he will actually lose his sexual power. Quite often this fear is groundless, but it is real nevertheless.

4. Homosexuality and other abnormal sex practices also have a deadening effect on the normal sex act.

5. Many men are so high-strung that worry over business and other daily problems will often

bring about an appreciable decrease in the erectile power of the sex organ.

"The fear of impregnating his wife is one of the main causes of psychic impotence. Fear destroys desire, and this fear is one of the most prevalent ones. With economic conditions as they are, married couples desire to keep the family small, and when fear of the wife's pregnancy is uppermost in the man's mind, he will certainly not feel very enthusiastic about the sex act.

"Lack of sexual cleanliness also drives away the sexual urge."

May it be said that any one of many strong emotions may upset one's mental equilibrium and so drive away desire?

"That is exactly the focal point of the whole problem. Any strong emotion, such as anger, disgust, fear or anxiety will often upset the power to perform the act.

"Often impotence may be the result of general insecurity and worry about important situations in daily life, such as inability to earn a living and fear of being inducted into military service.

"There is a group of cases in which the difficulty may be rooted in the personality. These are abnormal sexual desires, sadism, masochism, fear of venereal infection, and a feeling of sexual inadequacy. Another personality defect which may give rise to psychic impotence is excessive shyness.

"A common fear back of psychic impotence is the fear of injury to, or being injured by, the sexual partner. Lack of knowledge is often the cause of this fear. This is engendered by great love for one another and the fear to cause pain and discomfort.

"An opposite condition to this is what psychiatrists call conflicting loves. A man may be impotent with a woman because he loves someone else and does not know it. The person loved may have lived long ago, and may have been a childhood ideal. Many men who marry are so attached to their own mothers deep in the unconscious that they cannot give to their wives anything but the childlike love which a boy gives to his mother. In a sense that she is a wife, a sexual partner, such men cannot really accept her or treat her as she craves to be treated, provided, of course, that she, herself is normal. Frequently one sees such mother-attached men falling in love with women who want to be mothers. Such unions may be fairly satisfactory. They cannot, however, be regarded as normal sexual unions, and many of them go on the rocks."

Are there many such cases?

"A considerable number. There are other kinds of conflicting love, too, which cause psychic impotence. There is a kind of conflicting love which is not so easily recognized as the fixation on the parents or a brother or a sister, but which is almost as frequent. It is known that, in the process of transferring the affection which he first concentrated upon the father and mother to other persons outside the family, the child goes through a stage in which he prefers persons of the same sex as himself. The homosexual stage in the course of the normal individual's development is ultimately repressed, and is represented only in the sublimated form in normal persons as the basis of much of the sociability of later years. In many persons, however, this homosexual element does not disappear. Such men may marry and not realize that they are more homosexual than heterosexual. Of course, they are impotent in their sexual life because this homosexual factor looms large and forbidding.

"Finally, there is a conflicting love which is more powerful than any of these and also more prevalent. This is the love of self. Strange as it may seem, we actually love ourselves more than we love anyone else. We all love ourselves first, and last, and most. An overflow of this love is invested in others—wife, relatives and friends."

But is this normal?

"It is. In the normal person, however, experience enables one to see the advantage of drawing upon this love and investing some of it in the love of others, but in a great many people this process is inhibited. For various reasons—sometimes a lack of self-confidence, sometimes a fear of depreciation by others, sometimes because of painful experiences, sometimes because of faulty training—this cannot be done.

"For such people a true and deep relationship with another person is out of the question except on such a basis as feeds this self-love instead of detracting from it. Such persons may fall in love, but they fall in love with people who are like themselves, with people who flatter them, who feed their vanity and build up their self-confidence by a constant process of emotional nourishment.

"In the sex act, such persons may at times be very potent, particularly if the circumstances of the act are such that their vanity is flattered, their feeling of omnipotence encouraged. This is not real sexual potency, however, and such persons are sooner or later apt to meet with disaster. They are very proud of their sexual organs, and, indeed, it is not inaccurate to say that such persons prefer masturbation to sexual intercourse."

Most people probably do not know that self-love can be a cause of impotence but can anything be done about psychic impotence?

"Yes, indeed. A great deal can be done to correct it. Psychoanalysis offers a rational form of treatment for this kind of impotence. It is not a very easy treatment, and it requires expert handling. Psychoanalysis, however, well directed, enables the patient to become aware of, and repudiate, the unconscious influences which act as a deterrent."

How is a psychoanalytical treatment given?

"It is a very long and complicated process. Each psychoanalyst uses his own method. One of the most frequently used is the following. The doctor sits out of sight of the patient whom he interviews, to make the process as impersonal as possible. The patient is encouraged to speak, and speak freely. The doctor does not advise or otherwise tend to disturb the patient while he is unburdening his soul, for the latter must not be inhibited. His thoughts must flow freely and uninterruptedly.

"The patient is encouraged to think of himself in a purely impersonal sort of way. The whole process, indeed, becomes impersonal and thus the patient is better able to reveal his inner self. He must hold back no secrets. He must reveal his most intimate thoughts. At succeeding sessions he brings in reports of his dreams, for his dreams also contain very valuable hints as to his innermost thought processes.

"Several such sessions are necessary to uncover the repressed emotions and inhibitions which give rise to psychic impotence. The cure is not forthcoming at once. Various readjustments are required. But once the step in the right direction is taken, a successful outcome is possible."

Chapter 8

THE CAUSES AND MANAGEMENT OF FRIGIDITY

Just as impotence is the most common sexual handicap in man, frigidity is the most common sexual disability in woman. It occurs in about 60 per cent of all women. Frigidity is a sexual difficulty with many ramifications and a great many questions are commonly asked about it. The following are the ones which most often are asked in daily life.

What is frigidity as applied in the sexual sense?

"Frigidity is a condition in which the woman is indifferent to the sex act. For some reason or other she does not care for it; she is unresponsive to her husband's caresses; she is not capable of any pleasurable emotion during the act. For these reasons she does not know what a normal sex life is."

Is frigidity a rare condition?

"No. It is all too common. There are several varieties of this condition. There is a type of occasional frigidity, a condition in which the woman is partially frigid. She does experience moderate sex desire after she is aroused, and she has an occasional weak orgasm.

"This type of frigidity is caused by weakness, physical and mental fatigue. An unpleasant experience just before the sex act may change a woman's mental attitude so that she will fail to have an orgasm. Fear of pregnancy and lack of love for her partner may also bring on occasional frigidity.

"Worry will also have a deadening effect on the enjoyment of the sex act. A mind free from worry and distress is always a requisite for sexual enjoyment, and any strong emotion will drive pleasure away.

"Yet much can be done to overcome occasional frigidity. Attempts should be made to build up one's mental and physical stamina. The husband may be at fault. He may not know much about preliminary sex play that will get his wife ready for the marital act."

What is meant by pseudo frigidity?

"Pseudo frigidity actually means false frigidity. It is the least troublesome of all. It may be overcome with the least amount of effort. Most often it is brought about because the woman does not receive the proper amount of stimulation prior to the act.

"One of the most common causes is premature ejaculation on the part of the husband. No woman can respond to her husband's embraces in an instant. This is obviously a physiological impossibility. A well-known sexologist states that 40 per cent of the wives estimated intercourse to last less than five minutes. Many women cannot respond in that time, particularly if no attempt is made by the husband to arouse and prepare his wife in advance.

"In this category are also placed women who do not respond because intercourse is painful or even impossible, owing to such conditions as serious laceration of the important tissues about the genital organs, the presence of a thick and intact hymen, or a greatly relaxed vaginal tract.

"It is necessary for the husband to receive some instruction in this regard. He should know that intercourse is a matter for both man and wife. He should not be brutal in his methods. There should be a preliminary period of love-making, of kissing, of manual stimulation before the actual act is attempted. He should know that simply having his own orgasm is not enough. He must learn how to delay ejaculation till his wife is ready for her own orgasm. This can be done by ceasing the act just before ejaculation is to take place.

"The preparation for the act is most important. To overcome false frigidity in the woman she must be stimulated by her husband. It has been discovered that the most complete response in a woman follows systematic stimulation of her body. Touching and caressing certain areas of the skin powerfully excites sex desire. These areas seem to be related to one another so that if a certain order of stimulation is followed response becomes more and more ardent.

"These areas are all the manifestations of the endings of the cutaneous nerves. The nerves are the seats of all sensations and motor activities of all human beings. Under ordinary circumstances all sensory impressions are quiescent, but under the proper stimulation the sensory impressions may be multiplied and intensified. Once this is accomplished the sexual emotion is properly enhanced.

"All women possess these areas in various parts of their bodies. The husband whose wife is frigid should learn what these areas are by trial and error. Then he can learn to put to practical use his knowledge thus acquired and in this manner overcome his wife's unnatural inhibitions.

"Essentially, it may be said that pressure stimulation of these very sensitive areas will be of practical value in a great many cases. However, there may be instances in which this simple procedure will not prove of value. Mere physical stimulation is not sufficient. There is a very pronounced blockage in the pysche of the woman concerned."

The two types of frigidity you mentioned seem to be rather easy to correct. There must be other, more serious types. Can anything be done about them?

"Yes, unfortunately, there are more serious types. One of these is known as relative frigidity. Fortunately, this is not a very common type. In this category are placed those women who will not respond to their husbands, but will respond or in the past have responded to some other man.

It is quite evident that such a woman is not essentially frigid.

"The unfortunate thing about this type of frigidity is that it is difficult to overcome. Such a woman is generally neurotic and is unwilling to make the necessary effort for a cure. She is in the habit of claiming that she is mismated and the only thing to do is to change partners.

"The only possible treatment is reeducation. It has usually been found that the husband and wife are antagonistic toward each other. There may, however, be only petty difficulties at the bottom of these misunderstandings and these can be ironed out.

"If there is any degree of cooperation, and if the wife is intelligent and not too neurotic, an explanation of the whole situation may enable her to get rid of the particular complex that is inhibiting her."

One hears, also, of a type of frigidity that is paradoxical in nature, that is, the woman may have too much desire.

"Strange as it may seem, there is a type of frigidity of that nature. This type of woman may have strong desires and may enjoy the preliminaries intensely. Indeed, she is likely to overvalue the whole experience. It looms too large in her imagination because of the inevitable failure on her part to reach a climax. Try as hard as she will, the orgasm escapes her altogether. She always thinks she will reach it in just a few minutes more, but it fritters itself away, leaving her in tears, perhaps even hysterical.

"This type of frigid woman has her mind on the subject constantly and wants intercourse as often as possible. Her husband may cooperate with her fully and may prolong intercourse with her for an hour, but the final result is always the same. Consequently she begins intercourse each time with a feeling of desperation. She is convinced that she will fail, and this conviction naturally makes her failure the more certain.

"Masturbation is often blamed in cases of this type of frigidity. It is assumed that by premarital self-relief, the woman has conditioned herself to respond to clitoris friction but not to normal coitus; or she and her husband have practiced masturbation before they were married.

"The management of such cases is rather difficult. Coitus should be forbidden altogether for several weeks until the treatment is well under way. She should receive a thorough medical examination to ascertain if there are any organic causes which may account for her condition."

Are there any other types of frigidity?

"Yes, unfortunately. There is a group of cases which physicians term essential frigidity. This type is very complex in make-up, and hardly are ever two cases exactly alike. There are many causes and many reasons.

"For instance, one of the most frequent is that of the girl—a type mentioned earlier—who has grown up thinking that sex is something vulgar and indecent. She marries mainly for social reasons. The sexual side of marriage has been largely repressed in her mind, but, so far as she allows herself to think of it, she considers vaguely that coitus will be infrequent and only for the purpose of reproduction. Coitus for her is something to be endured and not enjoyed. She has entered marriage carefully, to be frigid, and she remains frigid.

"The next type is the girl who has been made to feel from infancy that this is a man's world, that women get the worst of it. Her whole attitude toward marriage is more mental than emotional. Her attitude toward sex is one of indignation and disgust. She is essentially frigid, and, though she may soon decide that she wants complete sexual satisfaction, the results of a lifetime of wrong education are not easily overcome. She is the most difficult of all frigid women.

"Now what is back of most cases of frigidity in women? There are certain difficulties in the lives of these women which bring about a condition of frigidity. The first great factor is FEAR. Under this heading there are quite a few subsidiary factors. These are:

"1. Fear of punishment (such as going back to childhood experiences in which sex was implanted in the mind and consciousness as a naughty word and a disgraceful act).

"2. Fear of being injured by the sexual partner. This is also the result of lack of knowledge and poor education in essential matters.

"3. Fear of pregnancy, usually unconscious and going back to warnings, in girlhood, of the danger of accepting the advances of boys. Conscious fear of pregnancy is extremely rare as a factor in essential frigidity.

"4. Fear due to a sudden shock in early life, as, for instance, attempted rape or some sex discovery for which the girl was emotionally unprepared.

"The second great factor in the production of frigidity is HATE. Under this heading we have:

"1. Hatred of the husband and the desire for revenge. Something may have arisen in married life which may cause a woman to hate her husband. She can no longer tolerate his advances and love-making. As a result, she becomes frigid.

"2. Hatred of the opposite sex, manifested in a homosexual trend. Some women may acquire homosexual tendencies which cause them to hate their husbands. Normal sexual intercourse then holds no interest for them.

"There are so many factors in essential frigidity that each case has to be considered individually. Thus the woman who is frigid because of fear of sex, growing out of an unhappy childhood experience, requires education along a new plane. This can be accomplished by a psychiatrist, who must go over her fears step by step and explain to her why they are groundless.

"The same holds true for the woman who is suffering from the results of sudden shock, and even the woman with homosexual tendencies. All of them require sound advice and wise guidance, and these can be acquired only at the hands of an expert in such matters.

"These women require reeducation and readjustment. Quick results cannot be expected in any case. The husband also must be taken in hand. His education along sane sex lines is important too. Prevention is much easier than cure but experience proves that the great majority of sexual maladjustments can be cured without any too great effort, if they are recognized as problems of emotional distortion or frustration and are dealt with in accordance with the accepted principles of mental hygiene."

Chapter 9

SEXUAL INFANTILISM IN MAN: WHAT CAN BE DONE ABOUT IT?

Arrested sexual development in man is not a very rare condition. It is met with in practice in every large city. Sexual infantilism implies that the sex organs have ceased to develop to their proper size and function. They remain small in size and appearance, although the man himself may continue to develop normally. Many questions are asked by those who suspect themselves to be suffering from lack of sexual development. They insist on knowing what can be done for them. Here are some of the principal questions—and answers:

What are the usual signs of sexual infantilism in man?

"There are several rather characteristic signs. First, the voice is usually high-pitched and lacking in strength. The face is devoid of hair. The hips are rather broad, and very often the man is overweight. The external sex organs are childlike in size and appearance. The man who is thus affected has no interest in girls. He is also incapable of effecting an erection."

Is there any way of overcoming this condition?

"Within the past few years science has evolved effective methods of dealing with arrested sexual

102

development. This consists of the injection of the male sex hormone, known as *testosterone propionate.''*

Just how is this treatment given?

"It is injected into the muscles by means of a needle and syringe. The usual treatment consists of three injections a week."

How long does it take before the patient begins to notice an improvement?

"After the sixth injection the patient begins to notice a definite improvement. He notes, first of all, that he is capable of having an erection. For the first time in his life he becomes aware of sexual desire. After twelve injections he realizes that he is beginning to lose some of his excess weight. His voice becomes deeper and a light growth of hair appears on his face. By now he is beginning to lose his feminine appearance.

"At the end of fourteen weeks of treatment he is a changed man. His weight is much better distributed, his sexual organs have increased in size, and there is a much increased hair growth all over the body. The sex urge, sex power and sex functions are now about normal. His voice is deeper and his energy increased. He feels like a normal male and he acts like one."

Does he still have to continue with the treatment?

"Yes, but at less frequent intervals."

Is it possible for a man suffering from sexual infantilism to be treated so effectively that he can marry and have children?

"Often, after a year of treatment, that is possible."

Are there other phases of sexual arrest that yield to medical treatment?

"Yes, a considerable number. There is mighty magic and healing in the male sex hormone. It is now being used to overcome all varieties of sexual maldevelopment in the male. In previous years, undescended testicles were treated surgically. Now they may be caused to descend and develop by using the male sex hormone.

"There was the case of a boy of nine who was brought to the doctor's office by his father. He was overweight and, for his age, sexually infantile. If nothing could be done for him at once, he would develop into a sexless, ludicrous creature.

"He was treated with injections of *testosterone propionate*. Within two months the testes had descended to their normal position, obesity was by now under control, and the boy was on the way to normal sexual development."

Can anything be done for the man who in his youth had an attack of the mumps which so affected his sexual glands that he failed to develop normally?

"Fortunately, yes. A typical case of this kind was that of a young man of 28 who came to the office suffering from eunuchism, or arrest of sexual development. At the age of 8 he had had an attack of the mumps which affected his sexual glands so severely that he failed to develop sexually to maturity. His voice was high-pitched, and there was only a slight down on his cheeks. His genital organs were infantile in size and development. His eunuchism, in brief, was due to the destructive effects of the attack of mumps on his testes.

"He was treated with injections of the male sex hormone. Within a few weeks there were the first faint stirrings of sexual feeling; there was a slight increase in the size of his sexual organs; his voice became slightly lower; and the growth of hair was stiffer.

"Treatment was continued for several months, during which time he continued to improve. There was further development sexually. His voice became deeper, his shoulders broader, and he found it necessary to shave now.

"Although he became capable of sexual emotion, he will not be able to overcome entirely the destructive effects of the attack of mumps he suffered in childhood. He is sterile, and will probably remain sterile. There is no sperm in his semen specimens and it is doubtful whether it can ever be developed. But the greater part of his sexual infantilism has been corrected."

Can sexual arrest occur in man even after he has reached maturity?

"Sexual arrest may occur in man at any age. Quite frequently it occurs during the male climacterium, or change-of-life period. Normally this arrest in sexual feeling is a slow, gradual process. However, it may occur suddenly, and when this is the case it is not normal.

"A man of forty-six presented himself at the office with a typical history of sudden arrest of his sexual power. He complained of irritability, excitability and melancholia. He was almost completely incapable of sexual desire. Treatment was begun with injections of *testosterone propionate*. This was continued for four weeks, during which time there was a noticeable improvement. His nervousness and melancholia disappeared, and at the end of three months he was sexually normal."

Does a severe illness sometimes cause sexual arrest?

"Yes, quite often. There is the case of a man of forty-two who had come to the office complaining of decrease in sexual power and premature ejaculations. He had been normal up till about a year before. Then his sexual organs began to fail in function after a rather severe and exhausting illness. Next, he began to suffer increasing fatigability, nervousness and irritability. Warm flashes occurred from time to time.

"He was treated with *testosterone propionate*, being given two injections a week. At the end of three weeks he felt much stronger, less nervous, and had a general sense of well-being. His sexual life also became normal once more."

What can be done for the man whose sexual organs are attacked by some serious disease, like, let us say, tuberculosis of the testicles?

"In such a case an operation is required to remove the affected testicles. The man becomes what is known as a surgical eunuch. However, he still retains sufficient male sex hormones in his system to keep him going for a while. But these, in time, become exhausted and we have another case of arrested sexualism. That is, we have such a case if nothing is done for him.

' "However, fortunately, much can be done for him. He can be given injections of *testosterone propionate* to supply the hormones which have been cut off. He will require such injections for the rest of his life, just as a diabetic requires injections of insulin, but these injections will keep him from developing into a sexual misfit.

"Sexual arrest may occur at all ages. It may be present as a condition from birth, or disease or accident may bring it about at any age. Formerly, sexual arrest and infantilism was regarded as a hopeless, incurable condition. Happily, this is no longer the case. Through the potent magic of the male sex hormone, even the most seemingly hopeless cases can be benefited. The sexually immature individual need not remain so; he can be aided materially and restored to a normal, happy sexual life."

Chapter 10

TREATMENT OF SEXUAL IMMATURITY IN WOMEN

"Sexual immaturity in women is one of the most common problems that the gynecologist has to contend with. It is a condition with many physical and psychic ramifications; it may be due to arrested development of the sexual organs or to sudden or gradual failure of the internal secretions of the ovaries and related endocrine glands. The questions that a woman suffering from sexual immaturity ask are those that demand an answer as to what causes her condition and also what can be done about it."

At what age does sexual immaturity in women usually occur?

"Sexual immaturity in women may occur at any age. It may be a congenital condition, or it may occur in a woman who previously had been normal sexually.

"Let us take a case of the second group. One of the most interesting cases in this category was that of a woman of thirty, the mother of a five-year-old child. She was anxious for other children, but she was incapable of having one. Something seemed to have happened to her after her first child was born. Her monthly periods became less frequent, occurring at three monthly intervals. She began to put on weight and was troubled with acne.

"Her condition was due essentially to the failure of the ovaries to secrete their normal quota of hormones. This accounted both for her irregular monthly periods and her inability to become pregnant.

"Treatment was begun, using pregnant mare's serum concentrate. This supplied the missing female sex hormones that her own body could not supply. Within a month she had lost her excess weight. Her skin condition cleared up. She improved mentally as well, becoming more cheerful. This treatment was continued for several months during which time she became pregnant. This is a type of sexual immaturity which can be treated with very gratifying results.

"Another interesting case of arrested sexual development was that of a woman of twenty-five who was presenting all the symptoms of the menopause, or change-of-life period. She had had a child at the age of twenty, and shortly thereafter she began to notice a gradual failure of sexual interest and feeling. She began to experience pain in her breasts and loss of energy; lost interest in her husband as well as desire for his company; was thoroughly miserable.

"This woman was treated with female sex hormones derived from the ovaries. Within three weeks there was a notable improvement. Treatment was continued, and within two months, her monthly periods were reestablished. She began to have normal sexual interests once more, and her sexual life was reestablished on a normal plane.

"Sexual arrest occurring in women in their twenties and thirties, and resulting in menopausal changes, is amenable to treatment by the judicious use of female sex hormones. There is a variety of these and each case is, of course, an individual problem.

What can be done for women who are congenitally arrested sexually, that is, whose sexual organs fail to develop?

"Considerable can be done for this particular type of sexual immaturity. Let us consider a typical case. A woman of twenty-three came to the office, complaining of lack of breast development. She was unmarried and her other complaints were that she had never menstruated, and that she was suffering from nervous irritability and hot flashes.

"This patient was 5 feet 7 inches tall, very thin, and weighed only 110 pounds. Her arms and legs were long in proportion to the length of her trunk. Her hips were narrow, her chest was as flat as a man's, and her genital organs were infantile in size and function. She presented a rather pronounced case of arrested sexual development, a woman who had never matured sexually because her internal organs were not capable of manufacturing the necessary sex hormones required by her body.

"She had never experienced any sexual feeling, was not interested in men, and never seemed to have been drawn to their company. The woman

had no male characteristics, neither had she
female attributes; she seemed to be a neutral
human being.''

How was she treated?

''Treatment was begun by injecting a female
sex hormone preparation known as estradiol ben-
zoate. After six injections there were tenderness
and enlargement of the nipples and darkening of
the skin around them. Injections were continued
and, after twenty-four daily injections, the con-
tour of the breasts began to assume normal pro-
portions. The womb also began to increase in
size, and the patient began to acquire feminine
characteristics.

''Treatment was now begun in another direction. An ointment was made with estradiol ben-
zoate. This ointment was massaged into the
breasts. They began to increase in size at a more
rapid rate. Contemporaneously with the injection
treatment, she made very encouraging progress,
gaining in weight till she weighed 130 pounds.
She began to round out and acquired the normal
contours of a woman.

''Her internal sex organs were also reactivated.
They began to feel the surge of new life. Her
womb increased in size, and the new potent chemistry that was created within her was gradually
eliminating the distressing signs of sexual immaturity.

''With these pronounced physical changes her
mental attitude also underwent a change. Acquir-
ing a more mature outlook in sexual matters, she
was no longer excessively shy, and she began to

evince an interest in members of the opposite sex.

"Her emotional responses also became more adult. She took a more serious interest in things in general, her mind became more mature, and her reactions typically feminine.

"As the treatment continued she improved still further. Her hot flashes were gone. She was no longer nervous nor irritable, but cheerful and bright. There is no doubt that sexual maturity consists not only of physical changes but mental and emotional ones as well. This was the case in the present instance and many others which have been treated along the same lines."

Is it possible for a woman to be sexually normal in all other respects and yet fail to experience an orgasm?

"It is, and this unfortunately is a rather common problem. There are quite a few women having their regular monthly periods, bearing several children, experiencing strong sexual emotion, and yet unable to experience an orgasm. It quite often happens that the first orgasm is not experienced till long after the first union."

Is this entirely the woman's fault?

"Certainly not. Many husbands erroneously believe that because orgasm is not absolutely essential to pregnancy, little importance should be attached to it. That is an error. The nervous strain, especially in a passionate woman who is not able to reach a climax is tremendous. This often leads to serious trouble."

What is a common fault in bringing about this lack of sexual feeling in women?

"The most common fault is that the husband does not realize that before the actual act is begun a preliminary period of petting is required. During this preliminary play the clitoris, the vagina and the vulva become engorged with blood. The clitoris, while important, is not nearly as important as most of us have been taught to believe. It becomes erect during excitement and it bends down to make contact with the entering penis. With the penis penetrating there should be sufficient lubrication to make the act enjoyable. In time the orgasm should occur."

What is the orgasm?

"The orgasm is the very height of voluptuous feeling and it corresponds with the violent ejaculation of the fluid from the various glands. Until the orgasm is reached the woman is in a state of continuous excitement."

What happens if the woman does not experience an orgasm?

"Many of the women suffering from lack of orgasm, experience more or less intense sexual pleasure at coitus, but do not get the relief that orgasm brings, and they are left in a state of frustration. Some of them realize the trouble, but many do not, and, without any reason for which they can account, they wake up in the morning unrefreshed by sleep, having a grouchy disposition, finding fault with their husbands, their children and everything in general."

What is the most frequent fault on the part of the husband in frustrating orgasm in his wife?

"It may be said that any condition which interferes with the full completion of the act of coitus may cause an absence of orgasm and pleasure. Prominent among these causes is the practice of *coitus interruptis,* in which the main intent on the part of the male is to remove the penis from the vagina before his own orgasm has been reached, and, as a rule, necessarily before the wife has reached her orgasm.

"Another cause is impotence or rapid ejaculation in the male wherein the male reaches his orgasm almost as soon as he touches his wife's genitals or shortly after the penis has entered the vagina. In these cases the male is through when his wife has hardly started.

"Another fertile cause of lack of pleasure on the part of the female during the sex act is fear of pregnancy, dislike of the partner, and a feeling that sexual intercourse is wrong."

Does masturbation have anything to do with dulling sexual feeling during intercourse?

"Yes. Masturbation, if it has been indulged in excessively before marriage may be a cause of lack of orgasm during coitus. In women masturbation brings into play abnormal channels of nerve stimulation, and as these are not stimulated during the normal act, the woman fails to achieve an orgasm. In most cases if masturbation is dropped completely and normal sexual activity substituted for it, the normal channels of nerve stimulation will in time bring about a normal enjoyment of the act."

Faulty Structure of Male and Female Sex Organs That Interfere with Normal Coitus

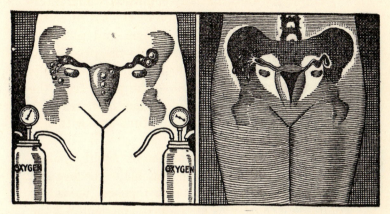

To test whether sterility is due to closing of Fallopian tubes, physicians blow gas into them, or inject iodized oil (seen in the X-ray, right), to see whether it passes through into the body cavity. Sometimes this opens the tubes and enables pregnancy.

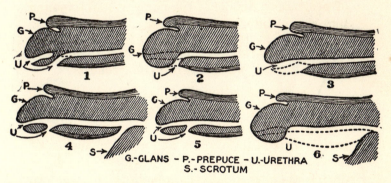

G.-GLANS – P.-PREPUCE – U.-URETHRA
S.-SCROTUM

Cross-sections of male organs, showing hypospadias in varying degree; from a slight case (1) which merely causes difficulty in urination, to those at (4) and (6) which prevent successful intercourse, unless remedied. In an extreme case, condition (6) may cause the child to be classed ase a "hermaphrodite" when the organs are also very small.

In rare cases, the womb has been **found** double, and pregnancy possible on **both** sides at once. This is normal in some **animals.**

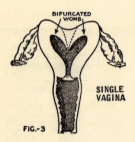

FIG.-3

COMPARATIVE SIZES OF NORMAL AND INFANTILE WOMBS

In many girls, the uterus never develops, as it should do **at** puberty, to normal size; this is due to lack of sex **hormones.** Such a woman cannot become a mother.

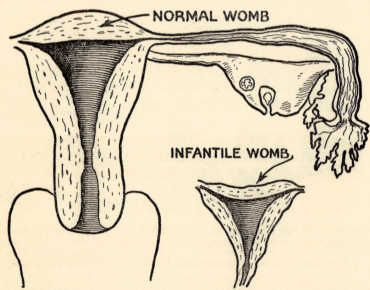

COMPARATIVE SIZES OF NORMAL AND INFANTILE WOMBS

How about abnormal conditions of the woman's sexual organs? Do they play an important part in destroying the orgasm?

"They most certainly do. Such conditions as relaxed vagina due to too frequent childbearing or extensive injuries to the birth canal acquired during childbirth exert a destructive effect on the orgasm. In these cases the vagina has lost all power to contract about the penis. Friction is reduced to such a degree that no pleasure is felt by the man or the woman. In such cases surgical repair is necessary.

"Conditions about the clitoris often result in lack of pleasure during coitus in women. The clitoris may not have developed to its full size, it may be abnormally placed, or there may be adhesions about it. Such women do not enjoy coitus in the usual position, but a little trial and experimentation with various positions may bring one to light in which the clitoris is stimulated and an orgasm brought about.

"Certain conditions, such as inflammation and growths in the genital tract may give rise to the condition known as *dyspareunia,* which means pain during intercourse. Pain when experienced during the act precludes the possibility of any pleasure being experienced. The diseased condition must be treated adequately in order to make possible the enjoymnt of the sex act.

"It very often happens, especially if the hymen is rigid or very sensitive that the very first coitus is so painful as to do away with pleasure during the act. In some cses the hymen is only partially ruptured, or ruptured so irregularly that for a time connections are very painful, and in some cases the woman actually fears to, or does not, permit the act to be repeated.

"Many women are normally frigid before marriage and for a certain period after marriage. This applies more particularly to a certain type of woman who has been brought up to consider everything sexual as degrading. In most of these women, if mated with the proper person, the frigidity disappears. In some of these cases, however, the frigidity continues throughout the life of the individual, but may disappear suddenly if the woman meets a particularly desirable man."

How can the sex act be made more pleasurable to the woman?

"Each case must be considered individually. Thus, in cases where the woman cannot come to a climax during coitus, but in which orgasm may be induced by stimulating the clitoris, a different position of the parties during coitus may be attempted, and in some cases the new position will bring the clitoris into closer contact with the male organ and thus insure greater gratification to the female.

"These new positions are a matter of trial and error. It is desirable to try out several new positions and to choose the one that is productive of the best results. As the sensory distribution is not precisely alike in all cases no general rule can be laid down that will apply in all instances.

"For this reason you must try out several new positions and the one that is productive of the greatest sensory stimulation is the one that will prove to be the proper one.

"It should be realized by all husbands that a little care and consideration will prove most valuable. Abrupt movements often prove disconcerting, gentleness is the key to success in this situation."

Chapter 11

THE TREATMENT OF EXAGGERATED
SEXUAL CRAVING IN WOMEN

For many years the treatment and management of exaggerated sexual craving in women has been a problem which many physicians and psychiatrists have had to face in daily consultation. Frankly, there was actually very little that could be done. Empirical remedies had been tried, but without much success. With the startling advances being made in female hormonology, this problem is well on the way toward solution.

The woman suffering from exaggerated sexual craving realizes that this is an abnormal condition and she is very anxious to know what can be done for her. What are the answers to her most insistent questions? Within the past few months these answers are more complete and satisfactory. Let us consider some of the questions and answers.

Is abnormal sexual craving in women a common condition?

"It is not an uncommon condition. There are many women who suddenly acquire increased sexual desire during and shortly after the menopause."

What is the sign of this increased craving?

"The most common sign is an increase in

weight. There is a direct relationship between the increase in weight and increased sexual craving. The increase in weight is due to failure of the internal secretions of the ovaries, the internal sex organs. During the change-of-life period these glandular structures begin to secrete less than they formerly did. This quite often leads to an increase in weight.''

Are there any normal variations in sexual craving in women?

"Yes. In some women just before the onset of the monthly periods there is quite often an increase in sexual desire. Most often increased sexual craving comes in cycles, perhaps normal, physiological cycles, at monthly or other regular intervals. This is bound up with the internal secretions of the ovaries.''

Is there any scientific explanation for increased sexual craving?

"There is. Briefly, it is this. The sex urge is controlled in women by the pituitary gland at the base of the skull and the ovaries, the internal sex glands. For some reason, perhaps because of physiological changes accompanying the menopause, these glands, or rather certain portions of them, become overactive. They secrete certain hormones, or chemical bodies, which exert an irritating or stimulating effect on the sexual organs. This irritation, of course, leads to increased sex desire. This being the case, if the patient is given something that will depress the function of these glands, the intense sex craving will be moderated.''

Just what is this new remedy?

"It is, strangely enough, male sex hormone **or** *testosterone propionate*. Science has found that large doses of it injected under the skin will depress abnormally intense sexual craving and bring about relief."

How is this hormone given?

"It is given once every two days. Quite often after the first injection there is some relief, but the treatment must be continued. During the first week, the treatment is given every other day, and for the next two weeks three times a week. In most cases complete relief is obtained within three weeks or a month."

Does the morbid sex craving return?

"In some cases there is a recurrence. If this should happen, another course of treatment is, of course, required. Some patients obtain permanent relief after the first course of treatment, others after two or three courses, and still others after four or five. Fortunately, most cases can be permanently relieved."

What about mental treatment? Is there anything to that?

"Mental treatment, or psychotherapy, was quite frequently resorted to before the advent of the male sex hormone treatment, but the results were negligible. Simply telling a woman to exert some will power to control her abnormal sex craving is not enough. The condition is more than mental. It has a physical basis, and it has to be treated accordingly."

Does diet help?

"Yes, but only in conjunction with the hormone treatment. In most cases of increased sex craving there is also an increase in weight. A low-calory, high-vitamin diet which allows 54 grams of carbohydrates daily, in addition to 9 grams of fat and 70 grams of protein, will help to reduce the tendency to overweight. This, however, is only a side treatment."

There has been a great deal of talk about sublimation of the sexual urge. Can it be applied in cases of morbid sex desire?

"It is true that the sex urge is a form of energy and that it may, under certain conditions, be directed along non-sexual channels. This is true when there are no very great irritative factors back of the sexual urge.

"In those cases in which the causes of morbid sex drives are psychic rather than organic, some benefit may actually be derived by using this energy up along non-sexual lines. In such instances, sexual energy can be converted into creative energy such as painting, writing and designing.

"Many of the great women writers and designers are those who have learned to use their sexual emotions along lines of creative endeavor. This requires great will power and persistent training.

"There are three directions into which normal sexual and even abnormal sexual energy can be diverted. These are 1. love of self; 2. love of others; and 3. work substitution. The last of these may be used in some cases of mildly exaggerted sex drives, with great benefit. Intensive mental or physical work will often exert a deadening influence on over-intense sex desires. The woman who is constantly on the go, who is active mentally and physically, will have little time left for morbid thoughts.

"Lecturing, traveling, writing and doing other work which requires physical and emotional expenditure of energy has often been found effective in nullifying unusually strong sexual desire.

"The fortunate thing about morbid sexual craving is that it can be controlled either by medical treatment, in the more pronounced cases in which there is actually a physical cause for this condition, or by diverting sexual energy along non-sexual lines, when there is no physical cause for this condition."

Chapter 12

THE TREATMENT OF EXAGGERATED SEXUAL CRAVING IN MEN

Variations of sexual feeling occur in men with great frequency. It is ridiculous to say that all men are endowed alike sexually. They are not. Many men are quite oversexed and, when this is the case, they are faced with a very vexing problem. Such a man has many questions which he would like to have answered. The following have been found to be among the most important, and the answers to them are given here:

Is increased sexual craving in man an unusual condition?

"It is much more common than is popularly supposed. Hypereroticism, or erotomania, exists in about two men out of every ten."

Is there any discoverable cause for this condition?

"Yes. The causes of increased sexual craving have a physiological basis. Often overactivity of the genital glands gives rise to a state of continuous sexual desire. Such an individual is actully sexually obsessed. He thinks almost continually of sex and of ways to gratify himself."

Is there any relation between priapism and increased sex desire in men?

"Priapism is a condition in which there is a permanent erection of the penis. Quite often this condition is painful and is not relieved by sexual relations. Priapism is caused by a nervous ailment and is not in any way related to hypereroticism. Priapism is involuntary erection of the penis, while the man suffering from increased sex desire is still capable of exercising a voluntary control over his sexual organ."

May it be said that an oversecretion of the genital glands is the actual basis of hypereroticism?

"Primarily, yes. However, all glands are under control of the nervous system. Coincidentally, there is also a constant stimulation of the nerves that control the sex glands. Both conditions existing at the same time, are usually responsible for morbid sex cravings in men."

Is it possible for a man of normal sexual desires to become hypererotic because of certain abuses?

"Yes. The too frequent use of certain drugs will cause exaggerated sexual craving. Narcotics, such as opium, mescaline, heroin and other dangerous drugs will arouse a man sexually far beyond his normal needs. Many sex crimes are committed by men under the influence of narcotics."

What about alcohol?

"Alcohol also arouses sex desires to an abnormal degree. Alcohol exerts an intensely stimulating effect on the nerves controlling the sex organs, and sex desire is so increased at times that the individual will resort to criminal ways to satisfy his demands. Dr. Pollen in his study of the sex criminal has found that drugs and alcohol exert definite effects in increasing sexual craving beyond normal requirements.''

What can be done about exaggerated sexual craving in men?

''Each case is a problem in itself. The man suffering from intense sexual desire which leads him to commit criminal acts is treated in a drastic way. There are laws in certain countries which prescribe castration and sterilization of such individuals. These measures are aimed to protect society against sexual degenerates. They are drastic, but conditions demand them. However, this is not the usual practice.

''There are various sedative drugs which have been used with marked success in depressing the oversexed individual. The bromides are usually the most commonly used. However, sometimes they do not prove very successful.''

What is done when they fail to give relief?

''Other more active sedatives are then employed. Synthetic chemistry has given doctors a whole array of new drugs which often give very good results. Among these may be mentioned sodium amytal, evipan, the barbiturates, sodium phenobarbital, dial and others of this type. In most instances relief can be obtained.''

Are there any hormones which can be used to depress the activity of the sex glands, as is the case with similar conditions in women?

"No. Although research is being carried on at the present time along these lines, there is as yet no hormone treatment for hypereroticism in men."

Are autoerotic practices, like masturbation, a solution to this problem?

"No. Masturbation often provokes it. No auto-erotic indulgence is entirely normal. It is best that they all be avoided. A more practical solution is for an oversexed man to marry an oversexed woman, but this is much easier said than done. Seeking out prostitutes and other women of loose morals to satisfy his great sexual needs will often result in a venereal infection."

It is sometimes said that vigorous physical activity often has a deadening effect on sex desire. Is this true?

"Yes, this is quite true. The athlete in training is usually not plagued by sex desire. For this reason, the hypersexed man should indulge in sports that require the expenditure of much physical energy. The more vigorous the sport, the more satisfactory will be the results. Sports very often serve as an excellent substitute for strong sex urgings."

What about other hygienic measures?

"Travel, and perhaps much more vigorous activity, such as exploration, is of great value as a physical outlet for unbounded sexual energy. Constantly changing scenes, new interests, new occupations, often leave little thought and energy for sex."

Is it possible to convert sexual energy into other types of energy? For example, how about sublimation of unusual strong sex desires?

"Diverting strong sex desires into fields of creative endeavor will often prove helpful. Writing, painting, intensive scientific research and other forms of mental activity will often go a long way toward curbing unusually strong sexual craving.

"Of necessity, advice along these lines has to be rather general. Each case is an individual problem, and it has to be treated as such. Some cases may require surgical treatment, others will do well under medical management. Still others require a regulation of their hygienic habits. However, all cases of exaggerated sexual craving in men are amenable to some form of treatment. It is best to seek competent medical advice at the earliest possible moment."

Chapter 13

SEXUAL NERVOUS DISORDERS AND THEIR MANAGEMENT

Nervous disorders arising as a result of maladjusted sexual living are rather common. They affect both men and women, but as is to be expected the great majority are women. This is because their nervous systems are more finely attuned and they react more intensely to a given situation.

The normal woman craves love and, if she marries expecting a normal gratification of her love, but does not get it, she is bound to suffer. The natural result will be a bad case of nerves. The questions that occur most frequently in the minds of men and women suffering from nervous upset arising from sexual maladjustment are usually those given below—with the answers.

What are the signs and symptoms of nervousness due to sexual frustration?

"There are several characteristic features. One is that the person so affected perspires a great deal. The skin feels cold and clammy, and the heart fails to behave in a perfectly normal manner. It skips a beat now and then. Sleep is not always possible at night.

"Quite often the nervous individual also suffers from what is called compulsive actions. They feel that they must count everything they see; they feel impelled to stop on every crack in the sidewalk. Occasionally they also suffer from phobias of various sorts: fear of high places, confined areas, crowds, etc."

What are the causes of sexual nervousness?

"There are many. However, the following list of nine covers the most common, and includes comments on each.

"1. In a woman sexual nervousness may be due to some structural defect in her sex organs. A thorough examination will reveal this defect. It may be corrected either surgically or by means of glandular treatment. Sexual immaturity yields very well to hormone treatment.

"2. There may be some defect elsewhere, such as endocrine gland disease, marked physical weakness, or some serious disease of the blood which may prevent complete satisfaction of the love instinct. In a great many cases, these difficulties can be overcome by appropriate treatment on the part of a competent physician.

"3. The husband may be impotent or otherwise sexually inefficient. Such a case calls for a thorough examination of the husband by a competent urologist. Most cases of impotence are now amenable to treatment. Glandular extracts given by means of injections have been found to correct not a few of such cases.

"4. The fear of pregnancy is also a fertile cause of sex nerves. Pregnancy can be prevented by any number of birth-control methods which are now in use.

"5. There may be a conviction, due to faulty upbringing, that sexual desire is a sinful thing. If sex is thought to be sinful, and yet if there is a natural desire to gratify this urge, the mental conflict that results will, of course, cause nervousness.

"6. The first sexual union may have been so painful that the woman still retains a subconscious impression of the occasion, and therefore dreads a repetition.

"7. Her first sexual experience may have been revolting in another way, so that she still remembers it with disgust.

"8. She may have a homosexual tendency which causes her subconsciously to hate men.

"9. An earlier training which engrained the feeling in her that too much thinking about sex is unladylike, may still be retained and act as a barrier against proper response to the act.

"Another fertile cause of sex nerves in women is the erroneous impression that there is a set rule as to the frequency with which one may indulge in sexual relations. Accordingly, many women indulge, not too much, but too little in sexual intercourse, with subsequent bad effects so far as their nervous makeup is concerned. The logical statement to make in this connection is that husband and wife may indulge in sexual intercourse as often as they really wish; weariness and satisfaction will be an automatic control which will prevent overdoing the act."

Just what can be done to correct the conditions

which cause nervous upsets in women because of maladjustment to sexual matters?

"Fortunately, a great deal. Structural defects, if they are not too serious, can be overcome. Most often these defects are due to growths, such as tumors. These can be removed and a plastic operation can be performed to restore the organs to at least a semblance of normality. When these defects are due to immaturity, the use of hormone preparations will often prove exceedingly helpful.

"In many instances, abnormal conditions elsewhere in the body can also be remedied by proper treatment. In cases of severe blood diseases, for instance, liver and iron will bring good results. Through proper diet and exercise general physical depression can be overcome.

"The husband's impotence is a problem in itself as a cause of sexual neurosis in women. By means of new methods now available, many such cases can be cured. Impotence in men is not the hopeless condition it was once thought to be. With proper treatment, gratifying results can be obtained.

"Economic conditions being as they are, many women do not care for any more pregnancies. The fear of pregnancy is one of the most fertile causes of sex nerves in woman. If a woman does not belong to a faith which frowns upon birth-control methods, she may avail herself of the services of a birth-control clinic. There is now a considerable number of such clinics, in various large cities, which can prove of help to women who want to avoid pregnancy. Although abstaining from sexual intercourse is the surest way to avoid pregnancy, there are other methods which a competent physician can prescribe, and which are comparatively safe and effective.

"When the trouble is due to a conscious conviction that sex desire is a sinful thing, the reasonable procedure is to make a study of the literature of sex, from the psychoanalytical, biological and social angles. Sex in and out of itself is never wrong. It is the abuse of sex that is wrong. If the proper authorities are consulted, these statements will be borne out. There are, and will always be, those whose main object in life is to preach the sinfulness of sex. Most of these strange people are themselves either wholly impotent sexually, or given to the most revolting sexual practices in the privacy of their bedrooms. Most busybodies are mentally unbalanced.

"The importance of the first night of marriage is one which physicians have been preaching for a long time. It is the husband who has to be told that the first impression is the one which will either make or break a marriage. Ignorance leads to pain and distress on the part of the wife; this may be so profound that a lasting impression will be left which may make a neurotic out of the woman."

Earlier, something was mentioned about the proper sex education for the young girl. Is this of much importance in preventing sex nerves?

"It is, indeed of the utmost importance. If the right information is given to a young girl, in the right way, she will avoid a great deal of trouble in later life. There is no valid reason why the proper information should not be given on sex matters. In fact, it is most important that it should be given.

"The condition known as sex nerves is not a trifling matter. The sexually frustrated woman suffers as much as any one who is afflicted with a serious physical ailment. The first sign is usually a loss of appetite, with irritation of the stomach, nausea and fits of vomiting. Later on, dyspepsia and diarrhea may further complicate matters.

"Headaches are another disturbance which, with palpitation of the heart, make life miserable. Insomnia is another symptom which is part of the general picture of nerve exhaustion. Perhaps the most distressing symptom of all, however, is worry—fear of the unknown and the unseen, the constant dread of mishaps and accidents.

"Hysteria is a later complication in the utterly miserable existence of the sex-starved woman. According to Dr. Sigmund Freud, hysteria is due to an emotional conflict between sexual urge (which may or may not be consciously realized) and sexual repression. Hysteria may take the form of some rather severe physical ailment. For example, it may result in severe heart pains, even when the heart is perfectly normal, and in agonizing attacks of asthma, even when the lungs are entirely without defect. Pains in the back and abdomen, as well as other pains and aches, also may be due to hysteria.

"It seems unfortunate that, psychologically, a

great many women, as well as men, are badly prepared for sexual life. The fault is mainly due to improper upbringing. Yet the parents are not to be blamed too much. It is more than likely that they are entirely lacking in the proper understanding of sex, and that they retain some rather infantile notions themselves. There is no doubt that Dr. Freud is right when he says that most of the nervous ailments of mankind are due to frustration of sexual desire.

"Nervous disorders in men are also rather common. There are various phases of the sexual life which may lead to nervous exhaustion. The most frequently asked questions are those that deal with the effects of excessive sexual activity. These questions—and the answers—are here given:

How can a person know when he is indulging in the sex act beyond normal limits?

"The frequency with which the sex act may be exercised within normal limits cannot be estimated, as a certain number of repetitions of the act may be injurious to one, and yet physiologically normal to another, more strongly sexed, individual. The effect upon the nervous system is the only reliable test.

"Erection is a reflex act, and it is therefore due to nervous activity. Frequent repetition going on to excess will undoubtedly irritate the central nervous system to an abnormal degree. Ejaculation, which is the final result of erection, is controlled by a special center in the spinal cord. Excessive irritation of the nerves which convey sensations to the ejaculation center may therefore be expected to lead eventually to an abnormal state of this nervous center.''

Does excessive sexual activity lead to really serious nervous diseases, and sometimes to insanity?

''Careful observation fails to disclose a single authentic case which would corroborate such a claim. It is true that sexual excesses may be found somewhere in the picture when there are organic diseases of the nervous system, but only in very indirect relation to such ailments. For instance, a person who exposes himself to frequent coitus without discrimination is apt to contract syphilis. That disease takes a horrible toll of the nervous system. It affects the spinal cord and the brain, and renders life unbearable. But these diseases are caused directly by the syphilis, once it is contracted, and not by sexual excesses.''

Are there not some persons whose nervous systems are somewhat below par, to begin with, and in whom excessive sexual activity may bring about some nervous disturbance?

''That is true. Ejaculation very frequently repeated is liable to produce a congested state of the spinal center which, as explained earlier, figures in this act. This may result in a state of constant erection of the male organ and prove very distressing. Such a condition requires careful treatment. Overeating, overdrinking or any other excess will cause pain and discomfort and bring about pains in the stomach. Moderation is the Golden Rule in all human activities.''

What may be said to be the most common effect on the nervous system of too frequent sexual activity?

"The most important and the most persistent effect of sexual excesses is general exhaustion, especially of the nervous system. Neurasthenia is the usual consequence. This is characterized by a sense of fatigue, associated with irritability. With this condition present, any exhausting factor—such as hard physical or mental exercise —is likely to produce an asthenia of the nervous system, that is, general weakness, or lack of strength. Sexual excesses certainly are a recognized cause of this condition."

Does the constant loss of seminal fluid have any particular effects on the health?

"There is no doubt that it does. Sexual excesses, naturally followed by abnormal loss of semen, result in an exhausted state of the cellular elements of the sexual glands. When, through sexual abuse, the genital glands excrete and secrete excessively, it is possible too, that the elements of the internal secretion are in a disturbed state. The body, being thus deprived of the normal healthful influence of these important elements, must logically suffer.

"In other words, it is not improbable that the exhausted state of the nervous system, mentioned a short time ago, is due not only to repeated physical exertion and to the exhaustion of the spinal cord centers, but also to the disturbed state of the internal secretions of the sexual glands which are no longer capable of supplying the body with important normal elements."

Does excessive sexual activity produce, besides neurosthenia, other nervous symptoms?

"Yes, but these occur most frequently in persons with a nervous system below par. While a healthy nervous system may stand up under all sorts of abuses, a nervous system very unstable in makeup will respond with a terrific kick-back. Hysteria may result in individuals with a poorly organized nervous system who indulge too frequently in the sex act. These individuals are, so to speak, predisposed to ailments of the nervous system. That is, their condition, to begin with, is such as to render them liable to nervous disorders."

It is sometimes said that in certain instances, even more serious results may be suffered by persons with constitutionally weak nervous systems if they do not practice moderation in their sexual activities. Is this true?

"Certainly, and for the very same reason as the one already explained. Chorea, or St. Vitus' dance as it is more popularly known, and even epilepsy, may develop in people with defective nervous systems who practice excessive venery, or sexual indulgence.

"Just as certain persons are born with defective pancreases, and therefore develop diabetes when they eat foods containing too much sugar, so also certain persons are born with potentially defective nervous systems which cannot stand up under excessive sexual activity."

A great deal has been said about masturbation. Just what are the effects, on the nervous system, of excessive masturbation?

"It is true that the injurious effects of masturbation practiced to excess are more harmful and continue longer after the habit has been relinquished, than those due to sexual excesses committed by normal means. Nevertheless, there is not one authentic observation proving that masturbation is the direct cause of nervous or mental disease.

"For instance, in such a nervous disease as paresis, more popularly known as softening of the brain, sexually perverted tastes and desires not infrequently exist; masturbation is then the result, but not the cause, of the disease. The act of masturbation cannot produce a gross physical change in the nervous system.

"Masturbation is undoubtedly an exhausting process affecting the body generally and the nervous system particularly, but the nervous system can be affected by it only functionally, never organically."

Just what is meant by that?

"There is a difference between organic diseases and functional diseases of the nervous system. Organic diseases are ailments which produce actual alterations in the nerves themselves—as, for example, syphilis, which produces softening of the brain. Functional disorders do not result in physical changes in the nerves."

What are the functional nervous diseases produced by excessive masturbation?

"The same as those resulting from excessive sexual activity along normal lines. Neurasthenia, hysteria and other neuroses will be observed quite frequently in a masturbator, and, as a matter of fact, even more frequently than in persons indulging in natural sexual excesses.

"The physical and mental exhaustion following the act of masturbation is a well-known fact and, when the act is repeated, prolonged fatigue with typical nervous exhaustion results.

"Another factor that has to be considered in masturbation is that it can be indulged in without a sexual partner, and this naturally leads to greater excesses. Obviously, this means greater exhaustion of nervous energy.

"In closing, it must be stated that sexual excesses can be considered only as a predisposing cause for functional nervous diseases, especially neurasthenia. The chief cause of such ailments is an irritation of the central nervous system, which lends to temporary fatigue. The disturbed function of the internal secretion of the sex glands plays, perhaps, a certain role in the exhaustion."

Chapter 14

SEXUAL COMPATIBILITY

The ideal combination, in any marriage, is two individuals who are sexually alike in their needs and requirements. However, this is seldom the case. Each individual is usually a problem unto himself, a very individual problem. His sexual needs depend upon a great variety of conditions, and they vary as he grows older. The question of sexual compatibility is a very important one. The mind of the average person is usually occupied with very definite questions on the problem of sexual compatibility. Here are some of the most troublesome, with their answers:

Is it true that not all individuals are endowed alike sexually?

"In general, from the standpoint of sexual endowment, there are three classes of persons: those of moderate sexual drive; the oversexed; and the undersexed. All would go well if each person realized his shortcomings and tried to live within the demands of his sexual cravings. Sometimes, however, an undersexed man or woman tries to overdo it, and disaster is the result.

"It is a wise thing to heed the normal sexual drive and yield to it at the proper time. If an oversexed man marries an undersexed woman, their life together is bound to be very unhappy. This is one of the real causes of divorce today. One of the first steps toward an ideal marriage is the mating of two persons endowed with the same degree of sexual urge.

"If an oversexed individual tries to adjust himself to the demands of an undersexed partner, he will certainly be very miserable. Similarly, if an undersexed man or woman has to adjust himself or herself to the demands of an oversexed partner, difficulties are apt to rise. The oversexed man married to an undersexed mate may feel that he must satisfy his urgings elsewhere, either with mistresses or in brothels. Similarly, the oversexed woman married to an undersexed man usually has a host of lovers in the offing."

What happens if a person tries to live beyond his sexual needs?

"He or she suffers. Here is a case of an undersexed couple who tried to live their married life beyond their sexual requirements. The man was forty-five years of age and his wife was forty. At the present time they are very happy, but this was not always the case.

"For a period of about eight years, between the ages of thirty and thirty-eight, he and his wife were continually at odds—quarrels, misunderstandings, disharmony. Sometimes these quarrels were so bitter that the couple seriously thought of divorce. There were at least four temporary separations. And all this was caused by one thing: their maladjusted sexual life.

"The fact is that neither of them had been strongly sexed, especially the husband. If they had realized this fact, all would have been well, but unfortunately they did not. They tried to live beyond their sexual needs.

"There was a time when the husband would gladly have given up all sex relations. He certainly had no need of them, no desire, and he derived no satisfaction from the marital act. He thought that perhaps his wife was at fault, and he tried extra-marital relations at times. But they afforded him even less satisfaction. He would indeed have willingly dispensed with all sex relations, but, as it unfortunately so often happens, his wife at that time became more sexually aroused than she had been in their early married life and, to satisfy her, he kept up these relations.

"It took them a long time, but they finally noticed that for two or three days, and sometimes for a whole week or longer after such relations, they both felt miserable. He felt weak and irritable, and she had a pain in the back and was even more irritable, than he. But it took them even longer to find out that their sex life was the real cause of their disharmony and strife. They thought, as was natural, that the reason sexual intercourse afforded them so little or no satisfaction, but on the contrary made them feel so wretched and miserable, was that they no longer loved each other. It did not occur to them that they did not love each other *because* they had marital relations. It was an unfortunate thing that they did not know that, in certain weakly sexed men and women, the marital act may have a disastrous effect on love.

"When enlightened as to their true status, they decided to give up sexual relations altogether. Almost immediately, the general relationship between them improved. Gradually they both became calm and serene. Their physical health improved and their working capacity became increased.

"They made up their minds to lead a non-sexual life, and since then they have not had any quarrels, nor has there been any talk of separation. They are are now the very best of friends. They do not desire, nor do they feel the worse for the lack of, physical union. Spiritually they are now more married than ever before."

Is it possible for two individuals to be ideally sexually adjusted to each other?

"Seldom are any two conditions exactly equal to each other. Even in undersexed individuals, there is most often a tendency for the sexual urge on the part of the woman to be somewhat greater than with the male partner. This accounts for the fact that, in the case just described, the man's wife was more urgently driven in the earlier years of their marriage than her husband. Another factor must be taken into consideration when studying the sexual urgings of the under-sexed woman. During the menopause, or change-of-life period, sexual feeling is much increased, even in the most weakly sexed woman."

Is there any sort of variation in the sexual urge?

"There certainly is. The urge varies, even in the undersexed. In men, it is greatest between 20 and 40, especially between 25 and 35. After the age of 49, the sexual power decreases slowly and after the seventieth year—in the undersexed, sometimes after the fiftieth year—it becomes entirely extinct. The chances for future happiness, in cases of the undersexed, improves when this comes about.

"One of the peculiarities of the sexual appetite in man is his desire for change. This desire is responsible for polygamy in certain savage races, and for prostitution in civilized countries. It arises from a want of sexual attraction in what one is accustomed to, and from the strong excitation produced by all that is new. This accounts for married men going outside their home for satisfaction."

As just explained, there may be depressed sexual feeling—that is, only a small amount of it—but are there causes of complete absence of sexual desire?

"There are a good many such cases. One man, normal in all other respects, was afflicted with complete sexual anesthesia since birth. He had been born with an entire absence of sexual desire, and it never developed.

"When he arrived at manhood, he had no idea of the sex act and he was completely indifferent to everything concerning sexual desire. According to his notions, marriage was merely a sentimental union. In time he married a girl of normal sexual endowment, who had urgently wanted to have children. She soon learned of her husband's disability and became very unhappy.

"The husband then became aware that there was something in marriage which he had not taken into consideration. The explanation of the sex act was meaningless to him. There was one solution for the normally sexed wife—either to acquire a lover or get a divorce.

"She had lost all love for her husband, and her sense of respectability was normal, so a divorce was the solution. The young man, now realizing that he was not normal sexually, decided to lead a single life.

"This is a problem that needs to be given serious thought and consideration by every man and woman before marriage is entered into. Marriage is a partnership that requires some firm basis for success, and sexual incompatibility is always sure to lead to disaster.

"If the sexual capacities of both partners are alike, or very nearly alike, whether they be over-sexed, normally sexed, undersexed, or even completely unsexed, their marriage will be happy and ideal. But if there are any appreciable degrees of difference, much unpleasantness and unhappiness will result. This factor, more than any other, is responsible for the great number of separations and divorces."

PART III

MARITAL PROBLEMS OF THE LATER YEARS

Chapter 15

THE CHANGE-OF-LIFE PERIOD

Every man and woman goes through the climacterium, or change-of-life period. This is a time of readjustment; certain physiological changes take place; essentially the period represents a slowing up process. The average person going through the climacterium is full of questions. He or she wants to know what is in prospect and how these changes can be successfully met. The following questions and answers will throw light on the subject:

When does the change-of-life period occur?

"The climacterium, or menopause, appears after the age of forty. It usually occurs in the late forties or fifties, in both men and women. In women it is a more definite change, a transition from a rather active period in life to a less active one."

Just what are the noticeable changes that take place in woman during the menopause?

"In woman, the changes that take place are rather definite. First, there is a more or less gradual cessation of her monthly periods. The flow becomes scantier and, after a while ceases altogether.

"Among other changes that take place are these. The breasts are reduced in size and firmness. Certain nervous alterations also occur. Sometimes the color of the skin becomes deeper. The hands and feet feel cold, no matter how warmly covered they may be. There may be a burning sensation in the soles. A very common complaint at this time is that of hot and cold flashes.

"Fleeting and indefinite pains become very common and annoying. There is numbness of the hands and feet. Headaches are rather frequent, usually appearing in two types. There is the thyroid type, a dull, prolonged, indefinite ache, which is worse in the morning and wears off as the day goes on. The second is the pituitary type, which is a severe, throbbing pain due to congestion in a small gland at the base of the brain.

"Nervousness also is common during the menopause. At this period such emotions as fear and worry are not easily controlled. Sometimes these grow out of bounds and there are more serious complications. Among these is acute melancholia."

What about the mental changes?

"Definite mental changes often take place at this time. The woman entering the menopause harbors the thought that the critical age has begun, bringing with it a certain loss of charm and attractiveness. She also dreads the thought that her sexual life is over. This is, of course, not the case at all."

Does the severity of the change-of-life period depend upon any factors in particular?

"The severity of these changes depends upon the woman's bodily and glandular makeup. The more civilized the individual, the greater is the suffering. In the average, modern civilized woman the change-of-life period means a slowing down of body chemistry and functions. Sometimes this slowing down is very pronounced with marked effects.

"In very rare instances, there is a terrific swing in the wrong direction of all the normal bodily processes. This results in a peculiar establishment of masculine traits. There is a slight growth of hair on the face. The breasts recede in size, and the other secondary feminine characteristics gradually disappear. All this is due to an overdevelopment of the ductless glands known as the adrenals without opposition from the other glands, the ovaries, the thyroid and the pituitary, which normally balance such oversecretion."

Then it may be said that the menopause is very largely due to changes in the activity of the ductless glands?

"Yes, to a very great extent. The internal glands concerned with the changes which take place during the menopause are the ovaries, the thyroid, and the pituitary, all of which undergo a cessation of their normal vigorous activity. The slower the cessation of gland activity, the more gradual is the change-of-life, and the better it is tolerated. However, when the cessation is sudden, the reactions suffered by the woman are severe."

What can be done to minimize the effects of these changes?

"Modern medicine is equipped, in various ways, to make matters easier than formerly for the woman going through her change-of-life period. For one thing, the doctor may lessen the suddenness and extremity of the changes by supplying the active gland principles which nature has so suddenly taken away. He may give the patient pills made from ovarian substance, or from a combination of ovarian, thyroid and pituitary substance. Thus he makes more gradual and moderate the loss of the body's own gland substances. He puts on the brakes and slows down the terrifically fast pace.

"The second course open to the doctor is to remove, as best he can, the stress upon the already overstrained organs. This method consists essentially of hygienic measures. Rest is one of the best. The woman going through the critical period should get as much rest as possible, both physical and mental. She should not engage in any exhausting activities.

"There are several simple hygienic measures that can be employed. For one thing, by means of baths the nerves are soothed, the circulation is improved, the skin toned up, and the general condition benefited greatly. The best type of bath is that ranging in temperature from 95 to 98 degrees F, and lasting for from 15 to 20 minutes. A bath of this kind is a wonderful tonic for sluggish skins. Absolute cleanliness is very important during the menopause, when perspiration is profuse and the subsequent irritation of the skin so common.

"This bath also benefits the nerves. Its moderate heat tends to exert a sedative effect on the entire nervous system. The warmth also allays various common but bothersome skin itchings and pains which are very often of psychic origin. When such a bath is taken before going to bed, normal, restful sleep will be assured.

"A different kind of bath is the stimulating one of a lower temperature, around 60 degrees F. This type is indicated, or to be recommended, in cases where stimulation of the skin and its glandular structure is desirable."

Does diet play an important part during the critical years?

"Diet is of very great importance at this time. Overeating must be avoided. It is wiser to eat too little than too much. A mixed diet, moderate in quantity, in which meat is used as little as possible, and vegetables in abundance, is preferable. Water should be taken in liberal quantities."

Should sexual relations be avoided during the menopause?

"During the active process of the menopausal changes, sexual intercourse is to be avoided, or indulged in as little as possible. There is at this period an increase in the blood supply to the genitals, and sexual activity tends further to increase the presence of blood, promoting the danger of hemorrhage."

What about marriage during menopause?

"Very frequently the question is asked whether a woman should marry while undergoing the menopausal changes. If the husband is younger and virile, it is best that the marriage be delayed because the ill-effects of the climacterium will be accentuated by coitus. But after the menopause is definitely over, there is no reason why the marriage should not take place."

Does the sexual urge undergo any changes during the menopause?

"In some women there may be an increase in sexual desire at this period, but under normal conditions this is not the case. There is some cause for any such abnormal manifestation, usually irritation along the genital tract, or it may be due to disease or to a tumor. In any event it is important that the condition be corrected at once, in order to prevent later and more serious complications.

"So far as the sexual life of women at this period is concerned, some unusual facts have been noted. Quite frequently, following the menopause, sexual desire may be awakened for the first time. Many such cases have been reported. It seems that, with the cessation of the ova-producing activity of the ovaries, their internal secretory functions have been increased, resulting in an awakening of the sexual appetite for the first time.

"In other cases, where sexual intercourse had been painful before the surgical removal of the ovaries, or before the onset of the natural menopause, after the menopause the pain disappeared and intercourse became pleasurable for the first time. In these cases excessive intercourse during the active changes should be avoided, even if it is a difficult matter. Hygiene demands that it is best to forego it temporarily, to insure future health.''

So far, discussion has dealt with the menopausal changes in women. Are there any similar changes in men?

''There are, but these changes are not quite as marked. However, within recent years, doctors have come to the agreement that there is a definite male climacterium. The most common change may be the enlargement of the prostate. When this takes place, there is difficulty in urination, and surgical operation is required to remove the overgrown gland.

''Some men passing through these critical years seem to be exhausted in mind and body. They tire more easily than before, and suffer a loss of mental and physical equilibrium. Functional activity is at the very lowest ebb and it is quite insufficient to carry a man along at his accustomed pace. Also, there is a distinct emotional upset.''

Is there any change in the sexual urge?

''Yes, normally, a man's sexual urge is lessened. This is quite natural, for as he gets on in years he becomes less vigorous sexually. However, there may sometimes be an intensification of the sex urge, due to changes of the activity of his ductless glands. With a little judicious management, this unnatural desire can be curbed.''

What about the hygiene of the male climacterium?

"Men who have passed their middle years should realize that certain changes have taken place in their bodies as they have become older. Their muscles are somewhat more flabby, the heart and other vital organs a little weaker. It is best to slow down, to take things a bit easier. They should be moderate in their working, playing and eating. By all means, moderation is the safest road to follow during these critical years."

Does this also apply to sexual activity?

"It certainly does. During sexual activity a tremendous strain is placed on the body, a strain which a young, virile, vigorous body can stand, but which the older body cannot. He should therefore be more moderate in his sexual life. As he gets older he will find that he will not require sexual satisfaction quite as frequently as in his earlier days. This difference should not be cause for alarm. It is a natural, physiological change which is acting for his own best interests."

Chapter 16

SEXUAL ACTIVITY AFTER THE CHANGE-
OF-LIFE PERIOD

The question of sexual activity after the change-of-life period is a most important one. It requires careful consideration by both men and women passing through these rather difficult years. There is a great deal of misinformation current about sexual matters, and in this chapter an attempt will be made to clear them up by answering the questions most commonly asked.

Does the end of the child-bearing period necessarily mean the end of the enjoyment of sexual activity?

"Certainly not. For years the strange idea has persisted that after the menopause or climacterium, the sexual life of the individual is over. The menopause means merely that the monthly periods of the woman have come to an end, and that the child-bearing period is over. It does not necessarily follow that sexual feeling is at an end. There is very little relationship between menstruation and sexual feeling. At any rate, it is now a well-established fact that the sex urge does not cease because the active child-bearing period has come to an end."

Is there any period in life which means that the sexual life of an individual is over?

"There is no definite age that means the end of the sexual urge. There are many instances in which men and women have been sexually active at seventy, eighty, and even ninety years of age. As a matter of fact, there are even cases in which children were born to couples in their seventies."

If more people realized that, after the prime of life, sexual activity is not necessarily at an end, would not this realization be a great boon to their mental and emotional outlook on life?

"There is no doubt that it would. If men and women realized that the climacterium does not mean the end of sexual usefulness, they would not get the idea that life for them is practically at an end. Dr. Kisch and other authorities have stated that the sexual urge outlasts the child-bearing period. It has been ascertained that sexual desire is in no way related to the period functions of the ovary. In fact, it is scarcely related to the ovary at all. Many women from whom the ovaries have been removed, because of disease, find themselves as sexually active as before the removal. When it becomes necessary to remove the ovaries from a young woman because of a tumor, this does not mean that she has been deprived of her sexual feeling. It means merely that she will not be able to bear any more children, but it does not mean that she will not enjoy sexual relations."

Is the same thing true of women who have passed through the natural menopause?

"It is just as true of them. Not only does sexual

desire persist after the ovaries have ceased to function, but in many instances there may even be an increase in that desire. It has been noted that in many women, just prior to and during the early stages of the menopause, there is an increase in sexual desire. Another interesting thing is that often women who had previously been frigid awake sexually during this period. Also, some doctors have reported that cases of pain with sexual intercourse, which existed before the onset of the climacterium, decreased considerably after the change-of-life period. As a matter of fact, in some instances pleasurable intercourse became possible for the first time after the change-of-life.''

Are there any definite periods in a woman's sexual life?

''Physicians divide a woman's sexual life into two great periods: the first is called the menacme, and the second the menopause. The menacme represents the sexual period in its prime, when child-bearing is an essential element. The menopause means the end of the child-bearing period, but not necessarily the end of the sexually active life of the woman.''

Does a previously active sexual life have any bearing on the change-of-life period?

''In general, a previously normally active sexual life has a favorable influence on the state of a woman's health during the climacterium. It has been found that women who have been married for many years, and who had borne several children, will pass more comfortably through the menopausal period. Spinsters and women who have been widows for many years and who have led sex-starved lives during those years, will have a more difficult time of it during the change-of-life period."

Are there any other factors that determine a person's sexual life after the middle years have set in?

"Several important factors exert a noticeable influence on the sexual urge during the more mature years. The most important of these is, of course, the health of the individual. General constitutional diseases, such as diabetes, tuberculosis, blood diseases and nervous disease cause a marked decrease in the sexual urge. Localized diseases of the sexual organs, such as gonorrhea, and growths of various kinds also tend to decrease sexual desire.

"Pronounced obesity tends to diminish sexual libido. In such cases the obesity is directly related to failure of important endocrine glands, and diminished activity of these glands causes a diminution in sexual desire."

Is inheritance an important factor in sexual activity?

"Yes, an important factor. There are certain families in whom the sexual drive is rather slight, and is so passed on from generation to generation. In such cases the women undergo a very early menopause, and also coincidentally a loss of libido at a rather early age. In such cases all other factors may be normal, but the tendency to an early menopause which has been running in the family for generations will offset all other desirable qualities.''

What about the psychic element? How important a role does that play?

''There is no doubt that the psychic element plays a very important part in the sexual life of the man or woman entering upon the change-of-life period. If one's mind is free from morbid fears and if the outlook on life is normal and wholesome, the sexual urge will continue undiminished, provided also that the other factors contributing to it, such as health and inheritance, are normal.

''The sex life of an individual who has entered the middle years has serious repercussions on almost all other phases of his existence. Success in marriage during the middle years depends to a great extent on a normal, healthy sexual relationship. Many cases of middle-age nerves or neurasthenia can be traced directly to a disordered and unsatisfactory sex life. Incorrect sex habits may also have an adverse effect on health.''

Can it be said that sexual desire is a form of energy and, as such, is capable of being directed into different channels?

''That is quite true. Sexual energy may be converted into work substitution as the most useful channel. Or it may be turned into less desirable channels, such as self-gratification. In this case it may assume such unsocial habits as masturbation and the increased use of stimulants like coffee.

drugs, alcoholic drinks, tobacco, as well as over-eating.

"Other forms into which sexual energy may be converted is erotic dreams, flirting, flattery or hero-worship. Still another factor in sublimation which few people realize is that misdirection of normal sexual energy may take the form of perversions. Inability to secure the orthodox climax of a union may mean that sexual fervor will become extensive rather than intensive. It becomes diffuse rather than concentrated. In such instances homosexual practices replace heterosexual practices.

"Dr. H. Dickinson, who has made a very thorough study of a thousand cases of woman's sexual life, found that sexual energy unused in the ordinary way turns into other channels. In two out of three cases this energy turns into love of self, with masturbation, day-dreaming and other similar activities as the most common manifestations. The diversion of sex energy into love of others occurs at a frequency of one out of every three cases. In one out of every three cases, useful sublimation of sex takes place."

Chapter 17

THE SEXUAL QUESTION IN OLD AGE

Not in all cases of old age is there a complete cessation of sexual activity. In couples who retain their health in old age there is still some interest in sex. What precautions should be taken by the aged in regard to sexual activity? Is it possible for children to be born to old couples? What conditions in the aged forbid sexual activity? These and other questions are asked by a considerable number of men and women who have passed their prime of life. The following discussion, through questions and answers, will help to clarify matters:

Does old age mean the end of sexual activity?

"In a general sort of way it can be stated that there is a distinct diminution of the sexual urge in old age. Marriage between aged couples is a common occurrence, and quite often this is a platonic affair—that is to say, marriage takes place for non-sexual reasons. However, this is not one hundred percent true.

"Pregnancy in women in their sixties, and even seventies, has been recorded. Old men have been able to become fathers in their sixties, seventies and eighties. Cases have been reported in which the monthly periods have been reestablished in women many years after the menopause had set in. It is hard to say what the body will do in old age. Changes are constantly taking place."

Then it is also not always true that the sex urge dies when a man or woman has reached old age?

"By no means does old age always mean the end of sexual libido. Not a few surgeons will tell you of cases of old men and women who refused operations on their sexual organs, for fear it would interfere with their sex life. Sexual libido is more common among the aged than is popularly supposed.

"We have already seen that the cessation of the monthly periods does not necessarily mean the end of sexual desire in women; nor does the onset of old age necessarily mean the end of sexual desire in men. Instances have been recorded even of increase in libido with the advance of years, and still other instances of the reawakening of sexual desire which had been dormant for many years.

"The possibility of abnormally enhanced sexual feeling in old age should not be lost sight of. Sometimes the sexual urge may transcend all reasonable bounds and become truly abnormal. When this is the case there is real danger to the health of the aged person. Sexual activity is a definite strain on the aged body.

"Disease has been found to exert a great influence on the increase, beyond normal limits, of the sexual appetite in the aged. Thus, chronic disease of the sex organs, like chronic inflammation or irritation of some sort, is responsible. When these causes are removed or corrected, the sex-life returns to normal.''

Is it advisable for the aged to indulge in sexual intercourse if there is an urge to do so?

''That question cannot be answered categorically. Certain factors have to be taken into consideration. First, a thorough examination of the vital organs of the body is required. Is the heart free from any serious disease, such as enlargement, leaky valves or calcification of the coronary arteries? If the heart is normal for the age of the particular person, the chances for an unfavorable outcome of sexual intercourse are considerably lessened. If, on the other hand, the heart has been damaged by disease, the excitement incident to coitus may cause profound exhaustion, or even death. For any such person coitus must be entirely forbidden.''

What about the condition of the arteries?

''The state of the arteries is also of much importance. If they are abnormally hardened, there is a definite danger. Bursting of a hardened artery is very likely to occur during excitement brought on by sexual activity. Apoplexy, as a result of the bursting of a vessel in the brain, all too frequently becomes the cause of death in the elderly who cannot curb their desires.

''The danger of internal blood clots is another factor which must be taken into account. Because of the naturally sluggish bloodstream of old age, as well as the many years of accumulated infective processes, the danger that there may be settled blood clots is very great. So long as the person leads a quiet life, these blood clots remain in one locality, but during excitement the chances that these may become dislodged are rather great. Once freed they become a floating menace. If they lodge in the heart or brain, they may cause sudden death.

"Other, and less dangerous, diseases are those in which the kidneys or the bladder is slightly damaged. Sexual intercourse causes an increase in the blood flow to these organs, and this results in frequency of urination and a burning sensation when the urine is passed. This may last for twenty-four hours or longer."

If, however, a person is free from abnormality and disease, may he indulge in sexual intercourse in his old age without any harmful reactions?

"When a thorough examination reveals both the man and woman to be in good physical condition, moderate sexual intercourse is not harmful. In excess, it is likely to be devitalizing and exhausting. However, in the majority of instances, natural satiety will act as an automatic means of curbing excessive sexual activity."

PART IV

MODERN ASPECTS OF THE SEXUAL QUESTION

Chapter 18

THE MENTAL ASPECTS OF SEX

The main difference between the sexual life of human beings and those of animals is that, in the latter, the sexual function is entirely physical in nature. There are no mental ramifications of sexuality in animals; in man, however, the sexual instinct is deeply rooted in his mental life. In this chapter the mental aspects are treated:

What is the fundamental difference between the sexual life of human beings and that of other living creatures?

"The fundamental difference is that, in creatures other than man the sexual life serves exclusively the purpose of reproduction, while in man it is directed principally toward the attainment of pleasure and sublimation.

"Dr. Sadger divides sexual desire into genital and extragenital. Genital libido is that desire which can be satisfied fully and completely by the sex act, on each occasion it is performed, resembling in this respect the ego instincts, hunger and thirst. If, however, people deprive themselves of normal coitus for a considerable length of time, the result may be very grave disturbances in the capacity for intellectual work. On the other hand, the practice which has recently found so much favor of 'living life to the full' may yield complete subjective gratification, but not seldom leads to the cessation of all sublimation and therewith to intellectual stagnation.''

What about the extra-genital aspects?

''In contrast to the genital components, the extra-genital can hardly be completely satisfied, even temporarily. It is these latter components upon which the insatiability of the human sexual instinct depends, and which give to the impulse its ennoblement and sublimation and, in the sequel, brings about civilization. Neither the genital instincts nor even certain of the ego-instincts contribute so much to human progress as do the extra-genital component instincts.

''Genital and extra-genital factors operate in a special manner in what we are wont to call love, possibly in its true form only in the first five years of life. There are barriers to the real satisfaction of love at later periods, those of the Oedipus period, of the homosexual, and those set up by Narcissism; hence complete satisfaction is often missed. At bottom, the object-love and self-love are in perpetual rivalry.''

What is meant by that statement, exactly?

''Dr. Ernest Jones, the English psychoanalyst, has given us a picture of this rivalry in the following sentences.

1. You thwart me because I wish to possess you.

2. If I do not wish to possess you, you will love me.

3. I will thwart myself, because I hate you.

4. I can love myself if I love you.

5. I love myself if I love you.

"There is thus a constant struggle between the two kinds of love—object-love, or love of something or some one other than oneself, and self-love. Only when they become identical is there any success. Thus object-love stems from self-love. Bearing these facts in mind, we get a true picture of the mental process of falling in love. We first love ourselves and, when this self-love overflows, we fall in love with someone else."

What is the social evaluation of genital and extra-genital love?

"Society demands of a man that he should beget children, and of a woman that she should rear them. This is why he has brought the genital libido, and she the extra-genital, to the fullest possible perfection."

The word libido was earlier defined in certain connections, but is there an even broader definition of it?

"Libido may be inclusively described as life's force or creative energy. This energy may be conscious or unconscious sexual desire, or any interest related to life's force. It was Freud who first indicated that children have a sex life, and that it begins at birth, not at puberty as was formerly believed."

Is libido then merely the sexual interests and forces of the individual?

"No, it is much more than that. First of all, it

is composed of four elements: heterosexuality, narcissism, perversions and homosexuality. Every normal individual possesses all these elements. Of course, heterosexuality predominates, but the three other components are still there.

"As has been said, the libido begins with the life of the individual and ends at death. In man's struggle for satisfaction, as is known from Freud's studies, he seeks to gratify himself in order to propogate the species. This instinctive urge, which is partly conscious and partly unconscious, on the one hand strives to satisfy the instinctive desires, and on the other hand is restrained by morals and civilization."

It was stated that homosexuality is a normal component of the libido. Exactly what does that mean?

"From Freud's studies, we know that a normal person shows a distinct bisexual period up to the age of puberity. The heterosexual then represses his homosexuality. He also aims to sublimate a portion of his homosexual cravings for friendship and other social interests. If he fails in this attempt at sublimation, he becomes neurotic. Since every person does fail in some degree, everyone is predisposed to neurosis. The stronger the repression, the stronger is the neurotic reaction, and in extreme forms it may be powerful enough to lead to mental disturbances.

"Stekel from his extensive experience has demonstrated the powerful role played by the psychic factor of the unconscious wish, or desire, as a plastic and synthesizing energy within the human organism. The wish to be a man may raise boys to manliness; the wish to remain a child hinders development; the wish to be a woman leads the young girl to femininity. When a boy acts like a girl, it does not mean that he has that kind of predisposition. It may only signify identification with a mother or sister.''

What about the perverse component of the libido?

''The perverse component of the normal libido consists of various elements: incest, sadism, masochism, exhibitionism, voyeurism, cunnilinguistism, anilingius, urolagnia, fetishism, bestiality, kleptomania, pyromania, nymphomania, satyriasis, etc. In other words, there are small amounts of these perverse sexual elements in every one of us, but they are repressed.

''Many of these perversions are clearly observed in the child, as demonstrated by Freud's investigations, which he called 'polymorphous perverse sexuality of childhood.' In normal persons they are repressed in later life. In the neurotic and mentally upset they appear in the form of hallucinations, and frequently in symbolic form. The continual practice of the perverse instincts must lead to some form of neurosis or psychosis, as complete gratification cannot be attained. Fortunately, in normal persons, these perverse elements are so thoroughly repressed that they give no trouble.''

What about Narcissism?

''Havelock Ellis has written an excellent treatise on Narcissism. This component of the

libido has baffled psychoanalysts for many years.
Even today it is not very thoroughly understood.
It was described, centuries ago, under various
names by the Egyptians and Greeks. Rousseau
wrote a comedy about it.

"Walder considers that the Narcissism of
Plato, Aristotle, Descartes, Kant, Newton, Spi-
noza and Nietzche has aided the development of
science. These scientists never married. They did
not want to give up their libido the heterosexuality, but sublimated their tremendous energy
into scientific fields. Narcissism means self-love,
and the cases of those famous men bears out that
definition.

"In 1898 Ellis first described this component
under the name of auto-eroticism. Freud, in his
three famous contributions to the sexual theory,
in 1905, also used the same term. It was Dr. O.
Rank who first used the term Narcissism. In 1913
Freud accepted this name, and emphasized the
view that primitive man like the child is frequently narcissistic.

"Stekel regards Narcissism as manifestations
of wounded self-love, and connects exhibitionism
with it, regarding it as a specialized form of
narcissism. O. Roglider considers it as combined
with fetishism. M. Hirschfeld attributes to it a
splitting of the personality, one part admiring
the other. K. Abraham regarded it as an infantile
characteristic, where the child considers himself
as the center of his narrow world, and where he
overvalues himself in it. C. Kapp regards ath-
letics as a form of narcissism. L. Ferenczi has

suggested that Narcissism is a part of the process of evolution, not only in the production of sound and music, but in the formation of the special sense organs.''

Since the mental aspects of sex are intimately bound up with man's creative endeavors, may it be said that sublimation of his sexual instincts has played an important role in civilization?

''Yes, there is no doubt about that. Man is able to utilize his libido not only for the perpetuation of the race, but also for the building of literature, music and science. This will be discussed more thoroughly a little later.''

Chapter 19

THE SEXUAL URGE AND LITERATURE

Psychoanalysts believe that all the creative endeavors of man are bound up with his libido. Creative eros, or the love element, is the dynamic force of artistry. On the basis of the true inspiration of love rests creative writing. Along these lines the following question-answer discussion will be of interest.

Is there anything in the sexual life of a writer that gives impetus to his creative endeavor?

"There is no doubt about that. All the great works of literature stemmed from the libido of the creators. Edgar Allan Poe was imputed to have been sexually impotent. Poe apparently was like his own Politan, a dreamer and a man shut off from common passions. This restrained him in his choice of subjects to a few compensatory fantasies, usually on the theme of frustrated desires, and it accounts for his tales of perverseness and perversions.

"His works arose from his lacks; his tales of imaginative science and deduction satisfied his desire for self-aggrandisement, becoming in effect a compensation for what he could not possess. Even his critical essay of poetry becomes a defensive rationalization of his instinctive and inevitable practice, a justification of his own lack of passion. Because of his impotence he was driven to drink, but also to write, to create. He realized that, being unable to create in his own image, he would create on another plane. He would create literary forms. And he was eminently successful.''

Is this phenomenon also true of other writers?

''It is true of a considerable number. Herman Melville, the creator of Moby Dick, was overattached to his mother; he suffered from the Oedipus complex. Leaving home at seventeen, he wandered, and wrote those sea stories to compensate him for his lack of love. All his writings were born of this urge to create, because his personal life was love-troubled and unhappy.''

What about Walt Whitman, who is accused by some of having been a homosexual?

''Walt Whitman wrote his poems in a most revealing manner. Some critics have called them the homosexual's atavistic subconscious memories of the men's house projected upon the present social structure.

''Theodore Dreiser's frank dealing with sex as a primordial and perverse creative force is an epoch-making act of vicarious liberation. His greatest novels, SISTER CARRIE, JENNIE GERHARDT, and THE FINANCIER are treatises on sexual liberation. They were attacked bitterly when they first appeared. In fact, no publisher would issue his novels, and he had to publish them himself.

''The sex-motive in the works of Sherwood Anderson is of a different nature. He was the poet of sex-obsessed America. Living the ordinary life of an ordinary man until he reached middle age, he then threw off all restraints and wrote brilliantly."

Have not some writers drawn heavily upon psychoanalysis as the source of their best work?

"Certainly. Eugene O'Neill, the greatest of modern dramatists, has always been a thorough student of Freud's sexual theories. His plays Desire Under the Elms, Strange Interlude and Mourning Becomes Electra are studies in sexual perversity, deep and penetrating. In the last-named play he confirms all that analytical psychologists have written concerning the universality of the incest-wish in the heart of man.

Other writers have been strongly Freudian in their leanings. Joseph Hergesheimer is at his best when inspired by motives that have to do with love, with sex, and with creative begettiveness. James Branch Cabell employs medievelism in his sexual symbolic writings. Jurgen, his most famous novel, was for a while suppressed, but now it is seen clearly not as a frankly erotic work, but as a masterpiece of sexual analysis.

"The older writers, among them Mark Twain, William Dean Howells and even Henry James were somewhat reticent about sexual matters, but even such matters had an influence on their literary output. The psychology of Howells is found in his sex-repression. The sex taboo was strong in him, as it was in Henry James. The society of his works is disgustingly pure because he was so violently sex-conscious. He regarded sex as trivial, not realizing that it is not peripheral and localized but, instead, tingling in all of life.''

Hasn't poetry been in the main a means of expressing sexual feeling?

"Yes, most great poetry has. The greatest poem in the Bible, Solomon's Song of Songs, is frankly sexual. It is the greatest of all love poems. It is free in expression, uninhibited—that is the reason it is great. Some of the greatest poets of the English language—Shelley, Keats, Byron, Browning, Tennyson and certainly Shakespeare —did not hesitate to sing of love between a man and a woman in its most intimate aspects. Among the modern poets Edna St. Vincent Millay is a competent singer of the sex life of the young. Her erotic inventions are extremely beautiful and intricate.''

But isn't the novel a more popular outlet for sexual expression?

"It always has been. The most popular treatises on sexual matters have been novels. Flaubert's MADAME BOVARY started the modern trend of the frank treatment of sexual matters. It was distinctly an adult piece of work, and it is still one of the greatest novels of all time. From it Emile Zola drew his inspiration, and in his day he was the frankest exponent of sexual matters. His novels became popular as soon as they were issued. In England, Zola found a disciple in the person of George Moore, whose two novels, A MODERN LOVER and A MUMMER'S WIFE, introduced the factual treatment of sexual phenomena after the style and manner of Emile Zola. Thomas Hardy, in his two greatest novels TESS OF THE D'UBERVILLES and JUDE THE OBSCURE, discussed sexual matters frankly. This was remarkable in the Victorian era, when generally all matters pertaining to sex were repressed.

"At the beginning of the present century there was a reaction against Victorian prudishness, and a new freedom was born in literary expression. Novelists threw off all restraint and wrote revealingly about sex. They recognized that sex was a great and fundamental part of human life."

Who were some of these modern pioneers?

"There was W. L. George, for instance, who in his BED OF ROSES, discusses the social problem of prostitution. His SECOND BLOOMING is an interesting discussion of mature sexual relations outside marriage, a phenomenon which exists in everyday life, but which few novelists up to his time had dared to write about. Another of his novels, URSULA TRENT, deals with the sexual life of a young girl.

"H. G. Wells, the greatest sociological novelist in English letters, is the author of a whole series of novels dealing quite frankly with sexual problems. ANN VERONICA, THE NEW MACHIAVELLI, THE PASSIONATE FRIENDS, MARRIAGE, THE WIFE OF SIR ISAAC HARMON, uphold the liberal view of sexual relations as affected by marriage.

"Among present-day writers May Sinclair in MARY OLIVIER and ANN SEVERN, Rose Macaulay in DANGEROUS AGES, and Beatrice Kean Seymour in THE HOPEFUL JOURNEY deal with various sexual problems quite openly.

"Even more advanced treatment of sexual matters has been given by modern novelists thoroughly acquainted with the theories of Sigmund Freud. D. H. Lawrence, in his Sons and Lovers, gives new meaning to the old story of son, mother and sweetheart. This is one of the earliest treatments in novel form of the Oedipus complex. The more daring writers have followed deeper along these lines and have dealt with the less conventional aspects of the sexual question. Proust and Gide were among the first to discuss sexual aberrations, in their novels. In the United States Ronald Firbank and Carl Van Vechten have written novels dealing with out-of-the-way sexual manifestation. Lesbianism has formed the theme of Compton MacKenzie's Extraordinary Women and Elizabeth Bowen's The Hotel. The most famous novel dealing with this theme is, of course, Radclyffe Hall's The Well of Loneliness which was at first suppressed, but which is now widely available.

"Sex pervades all human endeavors. It is the basis of creativeness endeavor in life and in literature. Indeed, it is the stimulus to achievement in art, science and in purposeful living."

Chapter 20

THE SEXUAL ASPECTS OF OTHER CREATIVE FORCES

Literature is not the only creative art that often has a strong underlying sexual basis. The conversion of libidinal energy into creative energy, along the lines of work may also take other directions. Dancing, religion, music and the arts quite often are heavily indebted to sublimated sexual energy. Some of these other outlets will now be considered.

It has been said that dancing originated primarily as a frankly sexual art. Is this actually true?

"A considerable number of students of folklore maintain that dancing was invented for the sole purpose of catering to the sexual emotion. There is no doubt that dancing was widely used in early times in religious and erotic ceremonies."

Are there any authentic cases of the use of the dance as an aphrodisiac, or means of arousing sensual desire?

"Ancient history gives us the case of Herod, who was so aroused by the sensual dancing of the daughter of Herodias that he fell madly in love with her. Another interesting instance is related by the Greek historian, Athenaeus, of certain ambassadors, very learned and far from frivolous men, who were aroused sexually by Thessalian dancing women.''

Does folk lore contain any examples of the sexual implications of dancing?

''It is full of such examples. Among all primitive peoples, the dance was used exclusively as an aphrodisiac. According to Thomas, there was a dance among the Wachands known as the kaaro, which was nothing more than a series of voluptuous movements, and it was used as an aid to courting. Among the inhabitants of the New Hebrides there are many dances of an openly sexual nature. The well-known Hula-Hula dance of Hawaii is nothing more than courtship in muscular rhythm. The Talmud recognized the dance as a sexual aid. We read 'The daughters of Israel went out on the 15th of Ab to the vineyards and danced, accompanied by songs, calling the young men to marriage.' Here dancing was openly used as a means of sexual attraction.

''In all of history are to be found instances of the sexual motives back of the dance as a creative force. In ancient Greece and Rome the dance was primarily used as a sexual aid. In India all women who lived for love alone were expert dancers.''

What about the dance today?

''Some dances today, such as the tango, are frankly sexual in nature. The jitterbug dances, which consist chiefly of the swaying of bodies, the lateral swingings of the trunks, the convulsive agitations and quiverings from head to foot, the tugging, twisting and pulling, are nothing more than muscular movements which have for the chief purpose the arousing of sexual desire.''

What about the sex motive in religion?

"There has always been a sort of strange sensual element in religion. Man first worshipped sex, in the guise of gods. The first conscious religious ideas of man strongly suggested a worship of the generative, the creative, force.

"In many eastern religions, a palm tree was a religious emblem because it is long, erect and round. Similarly an oak tree assumed religious significance. Everything which in any way resembled the characteristic organs of man and woman became symbolic of one or another diety, the Father or the Virgin.

"Today many of the practices in church and synagogue have an underlying sexual motive. St. Bernard conceived of religion as a love union. The Church is considered as the Bride of Christ. Frank eroticism underlies many acts of worship in the synagogue today. This is also true of the mosque.

"It cannot be denied that love and eroticism play an important part in religion. Many derivatives of religious sentiment are closely bound up with sexual emotion. Dr. Krafft-Ebing has said that religious ecstasy is closely related to amorous frenzy. In some cases of insanity, religion and eroticism are combined in a very characteristic manner. Among certain peoples, cruel religious practices are nothing more than the result of transformed erotic conceptions.''

Does sexualism play any noticeable part in the

*other creative endeavors of man, such as music
and art?*

"It does, quite frequently. Music is primarily
a sensuous art; it makes a direct appeal to the
sense of hearing. Psychologists tell us that the
five special senses, hearing, sight, taste, touch
and smell, all play a very important part in the
makeup of the sexual emotion. Hot, jazzy music is
first of all stimulating music. Biologically, all
music written in a fast, jerky tempo was for the
purpose of sexual stimulation. Music composed
in a passionate rhythm is capable of exerting
effects comparable to sexual excitement. Such
music, according to physiologists, has the following demonstrable effects: It increases muscular
energy, accelerates breathing, raises the blood
pressure, and lowers the threshold for sensory
stimuli.

"Musical literature is full of compositions of
an openly sexual nature. To mention just a few,
there are the 'Love Duet' from Faust, the Dances
from Smetana's 'The Bartered Bride,' the very
spirited 'Baccahanale' from Samson and Delilah
by Saint-Saens, 'Spanish Dance' by Granados,
'Juba Dance' by Dett, 'Scarf Dance' by Chami-
nade, 'Ronde Burlesque' by Schmitt, 'Ballet
Egyptienne' by Luigini, and 'Five Roumanian
Dances' by Bartok.

"Art often is motivated by sexual feeling. The
Taj Mahal, one of the most beautiful pieces of
architecture, was a temple of love built by a great
Indian ruler to the memory of his dead wife. The
paintings of the early Italian artists were often

actuated by sexual motives. To take but one example, there is the 'Allegory' by Bellini. This painting represents the sexual emergence of man. There is the idea of the perpetual semen, from which all life flows. The male and female sexual organs are painted in idealized and symbolic form.

"All creative endeavor of man has some sexual basis back of it. Not always is this apparent, yet it is there. The sublimation of sexual energy is one of the greatest driving forces in civilization."

Chapter 21

THE VITAMIN OF FERTILITY

Within the past few years there has been a great deal of talk about the vitamin of fertility. Many new and wonderful things have been discovered about vitamins. These elements of nutrition are now employed for the treatment of numerous ailments and deficiencies. From the point of view of human sterility Vitamin E has assumed great importance. The story of this vitamin, however, is still hazy in the minds of many people. The following questions and answers will give information along these lines.

What work has been done with vitamin E in fertility?

"Many scientists have been interested in the relation between vitamin E and fertility. The outstanding men in this group have been two American scientists, Drs. H. M. Evans and G. D. Burr. Their experiments were performed with rats, to which they fed grains, shreds of tuberous roots and leafy vegetables, bits of bone and animal scraps, and water. Rats were chosen because they get along very well on this type of diet.

"In order to determine the effects of any of the

foods given the little animals, special charts were kept from week to week over a period of years, not only throughout the life of the parents, but throughout that of their children and grandchildren, until a diet was found which resulted in lasting bodily or functional defects.

"In carrying on their experiments Drs. Evans and Burr struck upon a diet which, although sufficient in all the necessary calories and basic substances containing carbohydrates, fats and proteins, and rich in vitamins A, B, C and D, nevertheless lacked some important factor. It was found that this diet seriously impaired, and in time destroyed, the reproductive power of rats."

What was the most significant result observed in these experiments?

"Within a short time it became obvious that the females in particular were undergoing some strange process. While their first pregnancy properly ended with the birth of live animals, the second produced many stillbirths, or all stillbirths. Finally, even when regularly-fed males were used for mating, no births at all were registered. Pregnancy took place and the embryos developed for some time inside their mother's womb, but would suddenly and tracelessly disappear. The animals then came to heat again, but the new pregnancy again ended without issue."

What happened to the embryos?

"It became apparent that at some moment of gestation, the semi-developed embryos were absorbed by their mother's bodies. They did not die but were simply added to their mother's tissues. In pairing healthy females with males brought up on such a diet, no impregnation occurred, because, after five or six months of this deficient diet, the males also became sterile. Their sexual desire was not impaired in any way, but they were not longer fertile.''

Could this sterility be corrected?

"In time it was found that a few lettuce leaves or a little orange juice entirely eliminated the disease from one period of heat to another. The male already seriously affected by sterility could no longer be improved, but the female quickly became healthy again.

"These discoveries convinced investigators that green lettuce leaves and orange juice contain an unknown element whose absence in the diet led to sterility. This element was found to be vitamin E.

"After the first discovery of vitamin E in lettuce and oranges, it was also found in green leaves of most plants, in fruits of every description, and in wheat germ. Milk and lean meat also contain it. Unlike other vitamins, Vitamin E is not affected by temperatures even as high as 250 degrees F.

"The isolation of vitamin E presented many difficulties, but it was finally accomplished. It was proved that as little as three milligrams of the vitamin is sufficient to restore the reproductive facilities of a sterile rat. It was also found that the feeding of small amounts of the vitamin to the mother, or to breast-fed offspring, prevented the young from contracting the ailments common to the first few years of life."

Has this procedure been applied to human beings?

"It has, but there are as yet no clear-cut and definite results. Whether Vitamin E is the long-sought-for magic element which will restore a human being to a lost fertility, is not yet definitely known. There is still a great deal of work to be done along this line."

Chapter 22

ARTIFICIAL IMPREGNATION IN THE TREATMENT OF STERILITY

Preceding the question of the effects of vitamin E on sterility by quite a few years, was the question of artificial impregnation as a means of treating sterility. There is an interesting history, of many years, of what artificial impregnation has accomplished. Some of the high lights are given below:

Who were the first to use artificial impregnation of human beings?

"Dr. John Hunter, in the latter part of the 18th century, was the first successfully to impregnate a sterile woman with semen obtained from her husband, who suffered from a structural defect of his sexual organs. In the United States the great gynecologist, Dr. J. M. Sims in 1866 made the first successful experiment in this field. A sterile woman with a poorly developed womb was finally impregnated after many injections of the husband's seminal fluid. The physician tried the method on six other patients, but with poor results."

What is the primary indication of artificial impregnation?

"The infertility of the husband, established beyond reasonable doubt, is the primary indication for using extramarital semen. This means that, because the husband's semen is lacking in spermatozoa, it becomes necessary to go to other men to get the proper seminal fluid. Such a donor, as in the case of a blood donor, must be free from disease and in a healthy condition. In addition, his family must be free from any hereditary taints. He must also be of the same race and, some insist, religion, as the woman to be impregnated."

How is artificial impregnation accomplished?

"The proper day must be chosen. In general, the eleventh to the fifteenth day of the woman's menstrual cycle is chosen. The patient is placed in what is known as the Sims position, which permits the womb to relax and its opening to widen so as to facilitate the injection of the seminal fluid. Only slight pressure is required to insert the seminal fluid into the womb."

How often must this injection be given before pregnancy occurs?

"Different cases vary. On the average, it has been found, from one to six injections are necessary."

How successful are the results?

"Dr. William H. Carey, who has reported his experience with artificial impregnation, states that out of thirty-five cases twenty-one were successful."

Are there any legal considerations?

"In New York State there are no special laws governing artificial impregnation. However, other states have their own laws bearing on the subject, and it is wise to find out what they are before artificial impregnation is undertaken. There are no laws against the process itself, but laws of inheritance, etc., must be ascertained for the protection of any offspring.''

Suppose the husband's semen is viable, or 'alive' and effective, but certain factors make it impossible for him to impregnate his wife, can artificial insemination be employed, using the husband's seminal fluid?

''Yes. There may be certain conditions which prevent successful impregnation by the husband, although he may be perfectly fertile. There may be a defect in the husband's genital organs which make intercourse impossible, yet he may have perfectly norman semen. This can be used to impregnate his wife artificially. Sometimes the spermatozoa may be normal but lack sufficient motive power to migrate into the womb. In such a case, artificial injection is a way to solve the problem. There may be chemical or mechanical obstruction at the mouth of the uterus or womb which precludes successful impregnation by sexual intercourse. In such an instance, artificial injection is desirable as a means of impregnation.

''Artificial impregnation does not insure perfect babies, even as normal impregnation does not insure them. However, the results of artificial impregnation are just as good as those of normal fertilization. Abnormal delivery may occur when either method is used, but they are not more frequent when the artificial method is employed.

''Test-tube babies, so called, are no longer a

laboratory curiosity. Artificial impregnation is strictly a scientific problem which is being solved by strictly scientific methods."

A CONCISE DICTIONARY
OF SEXUAL TERMS

A

Aberration, sexual—Deviation from normal sexual activity and practices.

Abortion—Expulsion, from the womb, of the unborn child before its term, or due time, either spontaneously or through induction by medical or surgical means.

After-birth—The placenta and membranes which are expelled from the womb after the birth of the child.

Amenorrhea—Absence of the monthly periods of a woman.

Aphrodisiac—A drug or other means the chief purpose of which is to stimulate and arouse sexual desire.

Aspermia—A lack of male seminal secretion during the sexual act.

Asynodia—Sexual impotence.

Atocia—Sterility, when applied to women.

Auto-erotic—Pertaining to methods of self-gratification sexually. This is used to include such practices as masturbation.

Azoöspermia—A lack or absence of spermatozoa in the seminal fluid.

B

Balanic—Pertaining to the *glans penis* or *glans clitoris* (head).

Balanitis—An inflammation of the *glans penis*.

Bartholinitis—An inflammation of Bartholin's Glands, a pair of small glands situated on each side of the vagina.

Bestiality—Sexual relations of a human being with an animal.

Biogenesis—The normal process of reproduction.

Bisexual—Having sexual craving for both sexes: an equal mixture of heterssexualism and homosexualism.

Bradyspermatism—Very slow ejaculation of the seminal fluid.

C

Castrate—A person who has been deprived of his sexual organs, such as an eunuch.

Catamenia—The monthly periods.

Centromere—The narrow, neck-like region of the spermatozoön.

Cervical—Pertaining to the neck or narrow region of the womb.

Chemicogenesis—Use of chemicals to fertilize the ovum.

Climacteric—Pertaining to the change of life period in both men and women.

Cohabitation—Performance of the sex act.

Coitus—Same as cohabitation, sexual relation, sexual intercourse.

Coitus interruptus—Withdrawal of the penis from the vagina before emission of the semen has taken place.

Coitus more ferarum—Act of coitus in which the woman assumes the above or superior position.

Coitus prolongatus—Prolonged sexual intercourse.

Coitus reservatus—Sexual relations brought to an end before the male orgasm has occurred.

Conception—The beginning of pregnancy following fertilization of the ovum by the Spermatozoön.

Contraceptive—A device or medicine designed to prevent conception.

Copulation—Sexual intercourse, coitus.

Cryptorchism—Failure of the testes to descend into the scrotum.

Cunnus—The vulva.

Cypridophobia—An excessive fear of having sexual relations.

D

Defloration—Act of rupturing the hymen during the first intercourse.

Detumescence—Restoration of the penis to a state of flaccidity after erection.

Dysgenesis—A term including sterility and infertility.

Dysmenorrhea—Painful monthly periods.

Dyspareunia—Painful sexual intercourse in women.

E

Ectopic pregnancy—Pregnancy taking place outside the womb.

Effeminate—A term applied to men having woman-like characteristics.

Ejaculate—To discharge the seminal fluid during sexual intercourse.

Ejaculatio ante portem—Ejaculation occurring before the penis has entered the vagina.

Ejaculatio precipitata—Immediate ejaculation occurring upon erection.

Ejaculatio precox—Premature ejaculation of semen.

Erethism—Stimulation of the genital organs.

Eros—The Greek God of Love.

Erotic—Pertaining to sexual love.

Eunuch—A man who has been deprived of his genital organs.

Eunuchoid—Pertaining or resembling eunuchism.

F

Fecundate—To fertilize, to impregnate.

Fetishism—The endowment with sexual qualities of a non-sexual object. Thus gloves or shoes may arouse sexual feeling in certain men. The gloves or shoes are then called fetishes.

Flagellation—Arousing sexual desire by being whipped or spanked.

Folliculin—The female sex hormone which regulates the monthly periods.

Foreplay—Petting and caressing which precedes the sex act.

Frigidity—A condition of partial or complete indifference to sexual matters. Lack of sexual feeling.

G

Gestation—Pregnancy.

Gonococcus—The germ that causes gonorrhea.

Gravida—A pregnant woman.

Gynecomania—Excessive sexual desire in men.

H

Hermaphrodite—A person having the sexual characteristics of both a man and a woman.

Heterosexual—Sexual feeling for the opposite sex—normal sexual love.

Hiatus—The vulva.

Homosexual—Sexual feeling for members of the same sex—abnormal sexual love.

I

Immissio penis—The act of introducing the penis into the vaginal canal.

Impotentia coeundi—Inability of the male to have sexual relations.

Impotentia erigendi—Lack of power of the male to have an erection.

Impotentia generandi—Sterility: the inability to beget children.

Incest—Sexual relations between very near blood relations, such as brother and sister, father and daughter, etc.

K

Karezza—A method of prolonged sexual intercourse during which time ejaculation is voluntarily withheld.

Kleptolagnia—Stealing for the purpose of obtaining sexual gratification.

L

Lesbianism—Homosexual love among women. Other terms used are tribadism and sapphism.

Libido—Sexual desire and all its implications.

Lochia—The discharge from the womb following childbirth.

Lubric—Lewd, lustful, sexual.

Luetic—Pertaining to syphilis.

M

Marital—Pertaining to marriage.

Masochism—Sexual satisfaction derived from being beaten, humiliated and harshly handled in a variety of ways.

Masochist—A person suffering from masochism.

Menses—The monthly periods.

Miscegenation—Marriage between two persons of different races.

Misogamy—Fear of marriage.

Muliebria—The female sexual organs.

N

Nymphomania—Suffering from excessive sexual desire, on the part of a woman.

O

Oligospermia—A decrease in the number of spermatozoa present in the seminal fluid.

Onanism—Masturbation.

Orchitis—Inflammation of the testicle.

Orgasm—The height of sexual feeling.

Orgasmus precox—Premature orgasm; orgasm occurring before the normal time.

Osmolagnia—Sexual desire aroused by odors.

Ovulation—The process of producing ova by the ovaries in the female.

P

Penis—The male sex organ.

Placenta—The afterbirth.

Pollution—Involuntary emission of seminal fluid, occurring usually during sleep.

Polyspermia—More than the usual amount of seminal secretion.

Pornographic—A term applied to literature, paintings, dramatic and cinematic shows which aim to arouse sexual desire.

Prevenceptive—Same as contraceptive, aimed at preventing pregnancy.

Priapism—An abnormal and painful erection of the penis, independent of sexual desire.

Priapitis—An inflammatory condition of the penis.

Priapus—The penis.

Psycholagny—Achieving sexual satisfaction by conjuring up in one's mind erotic scenes.

Pudenda—The external genitals of the female.

Pudic—Relating to the sexual organs.

R

Retifism—A form of fetishism in which the shoe is endowed with sexual significance.

Ridgel—A man whose testes have been removed.

Rugae—The transverse vaginal folds which allow the vaginal canal to expand during childbirth.

S

Sadism—A form of sexual perversion in which gratification is obtained sexually by inflicting pain on another person.

Sadist—A person practising sadism; a sexual pervert.

Sapphism—Homosexual relations between women.

Sapphist—A woman homosexual.

Satyriasis—Morbid and excessive sexual craving in men.

Semenuria—Leakage of the seminal fluid into the urine.

Semination—The process of introducing semen into the vagina and womb; insemination is also a term for the same process.

Sexologist—An expert in the science of sexology.

Sexology—The scientific study of sex and its phenomena.

Sexual aberrations—A term which includes all sexual abnormal practices.

Sexual anesthesia—Complete absence of all sexual feeling and emotion.

Skene's Glands—Two glands situated in the urethra of the female. Together with Bartolin's glands they furnish the lubricating fluid for the genital tract.

Sodomy—Abnormal sexual intercourse in which the anus is employed.

Spado—A person suffering from sexual impotence.

Sublimation—Diversion of sexual energy into non-sexual channels.

Summa libido—The greatest height of sexual feeling.

Syngamy—The process of union of the gametes during fertilization.

T

Tempus ageneseos—The safe period, taken advantage of in natural birth control.

Tenigo—Extreme sexual desire.

Testicond—The condition of having undescended testes.

Test-tube baby—A baby born as the result of artificial insemination.

Tribade—A woman homosexual, same as Lesbian.

Tumefaction—The process of erection of the penis.

U

Urning—A male homosexual.

Urnism—Male homosexuality.

Uterine frenzy—Nymphomania; excessive sexual desire in women.

Uterus—The womb.

V

Vagina—The female sexual passage or canal.

Vaginal—Pertaining to the vagina.

Vampirism—A condition in which sexual excitement is accompanied by scratching and blood-letting.

Venery—Sexual intercourse.

Virilia—The male sex organs.

Viripotent—Sexual maturity applied to men.

Vita sexualis—The sex life of the individual.

Voyeurism—A sexual abnormality in which the person afflicted obtains sexual gratification by looking at the sexual organs of another person.

Vulva—The female external sexual organs.

Vulval—Pertaining to the vulva.

Z

Zoolagnia—Sexual attraction to animals; a form of sexual aberration.

Zoosperm—A spermatozoön.